MIND WORKS
BRAIN TRAINING

Right-brain Puzzles

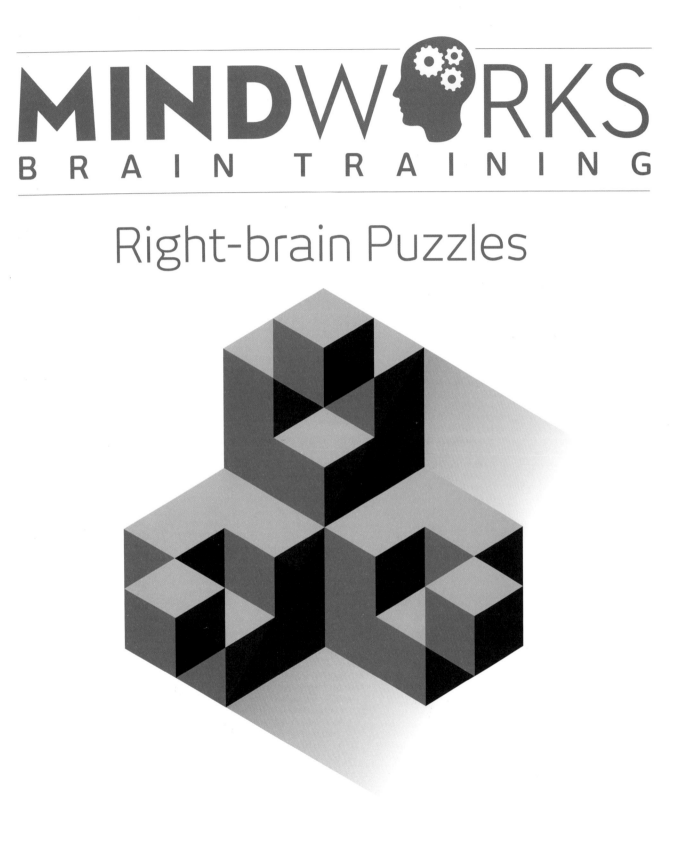

Published by Hinkler Books Pty Ltd
45–55 Fairchild Street
Heatherton Victoria 3202 Australia
www.hinkler.com

hinkler

Cover design: Sam Grimmer and Hinkler Studio
Internal design: Book Creation and Hinkler Design Studio
Prepress: Splitting Image

Printed and bound in China

978 1 4889 1326 6

Right-brain Puzzles Introduction

P Do you ever struggle to work out which of your keys fits your front door, or worry about squeezing your car into a tight spot? Do you envy those friends of yours who can pack everything they need into an impossibly small bag? Would you like to improve your memory and get in touch with your creative side? All these abilities depend on the right-hand hemisphere of your brain – the center of visual cognition and perception, and the source of skills such as spatial awareness, musical talent and imagination. "Use it or lose it" applies just as much to your mind as it does to your muscles – the more you practice a particular activity, the better you'll become at it. So, if you want to improve any (or all) of these abilities, the best way to do it is to train the area of your brain responsible for those abilities – the right hemisphere. This collection includes everything you need to do just that!

Perceptual Puzzles is designed to hone your 3-D cognition, your memory and your ability to see the bigger picture – mazes, spot-the-difference puzzles and dice and domino games will help you train your brain to look past abstract shapes and patterns and focus on the overarching principles employed in each challenge.

Spatial Puzzles is for those who want to improve their spatial awareness – here you'll find geometry-based games designed to improve your ability to perceive things in three dimensions. You'll be astounded by the difference these exercises will make to the way you see and understand the world around you!

This special edition of *Mindworks Brain Training Right-Brain Puzzles* includes a BONUS 25 per cent more puzzles to extend your right-brain training even further! Focussing on visual puzzles, like pattern recognition, mazes, memory tests, and more, these puzzles helps improve your ability to recognize patterns, make connections, engage your creativity and look beyond the obvious.

Just like training your body, training your mind is most effective when you actually enjoy doing it. That's why this collection of puzzles is designed to be fun, even addictive! You won't even realize you're breaking a mental sweat! Every puzzle is rated by difficulty on a scale of 1–10 stars, so you can choose to tackle them in their current order, or start with the one-star challenges and work your way up to the ten-star challenges. Each puzzle comes with its own time limit too, to keep you on your toes! But if you get stuck, there's no need to worry – answers are included at the back of each section.

CONTENTS

MINDWORKS
BRAIN TRAINING

Perceptual Puzzles

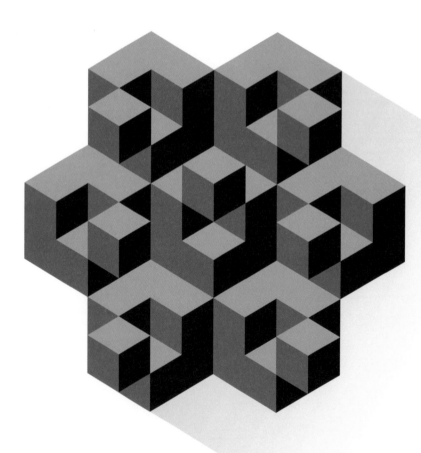

erceptual Puzzles is a fun and challenging collection of brainteasers for anyone who wants to get a new angle on their 3-D skills or the geometry behind shape-based games. There is plenty for everyone in this section, as the puzzles require different levels of skill and amounts of time to complete.

Most of the skills you'll be using on these puzzles come from the right-hand side of your brain, which controls the left-hand side of your body. Right-hemisphere skills include gestalt (insight, the ability to see the big picture), 3-D formations, awareness of color and shape, musical talent, imagination, and (believe it or not!) daydreaming.

Our perceptual skills are not as consciously tested as vocabulary or mathematical abilities. Being able to squeeze your car through a tight space or work out which key fits your front door are just two examples of how our everyday unconscious uses visual cognition. Despite the obvious practical applications, there is something unnerving about testing these skills—it seems that without the comfort of words and numbers to help us, we are in a different world where we have to look beyond the obvious. Colors, spacing, lines, corners, directions, and arrangement could all have an effect on the answer—but which ones are relevant?

The trick, therefore, is to look beyond the illustrations and focus on the principles being employed. Don't let the abstract shapes and unfamiliar patterns fool you, for the principle behind each and every puzzle here is relatively straightforward.

Our crack team of puzzle-constructors has carefully crafted a spectacular range of challenges. Not all the obstacles around this course are the same. The star grading assigned to each puzzle in the book tells you what kind of territory to expect—a low number of stars indicates that you're on an easier slope. But if you're tackling an eight-, nine-, or ten-star problem, expect to get your heavy-duty boots and pickax out, for these are the hardest of all to work through. Each puzzle has also been given a time target rating as well, so you've got to keep an eye on the clock. However, keep in mind that both difficulty ratings and target times are based on an average performance, so don't be surprised if you sail through a ten-star puzzle or find yourself struggling with a three-star—everyone is different.

So have fun while rolling dice, completing sets, toppling dominoes, tracking through the mazes, and spotting those differences. If you think help is needed, the answers section is on constant standby. Every question is numbered and has its answer clearly marked in the back of the section. But be sure to try all avenues before resorting to the solutions—things are not always what they seem at first!

With patience and practice, by the end of *Perceptual Puzzles*, you'll be looking at the world in a whole new light ✿

—Alison Moore

1 DIFFICULTY ●●●☆☆☆☆☆☆
Target time: 5 minutes

Find your way from the front of the house to the back.

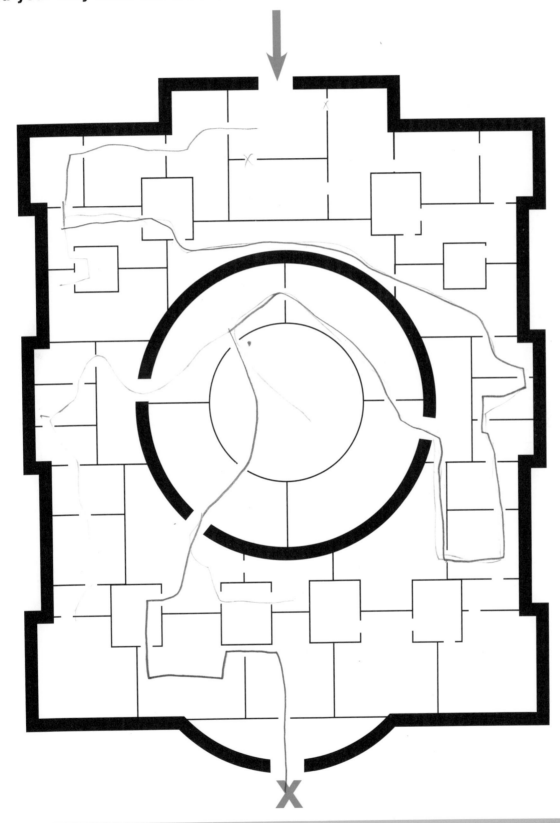

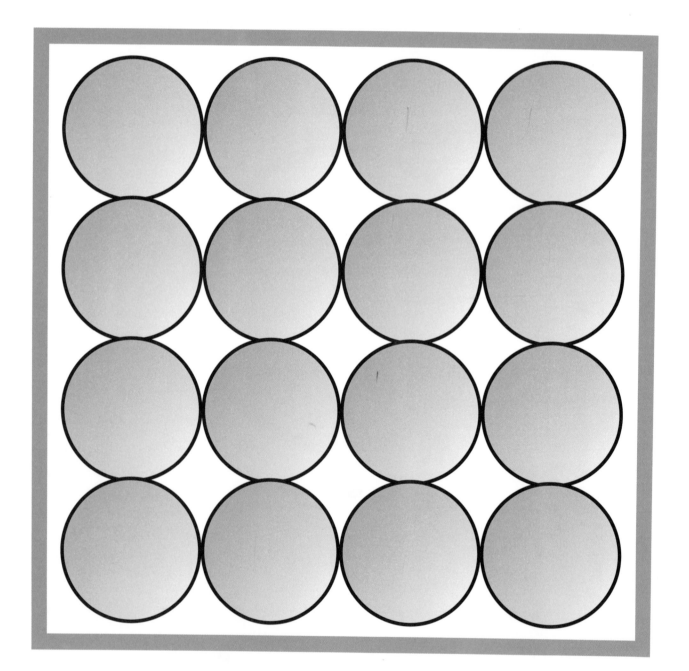

2 DIFFICULTY ⭐⭐⭐⭐⭐☆☆☆☆☆
Target time: 5 minutes

This is a two-player game. Players take turns removing either one coin or two touching coins. The winner is the person who picks up the last coin. Once you've played the game a few times, see if you can work out how to guarantee a win if your opponent plays first.

3 DIFFICULTY ✪✪✪✪✪✪☆☆☆
Target time: 5 minutes

Study the letters below for one minute, then see if you can answer the questions on the next page without checking back.

4 DIFFICULTY ✪✪✪☆☆☆☆☆☆
Target time: 3 minutes

Can you spot the eight differences between these two pictures? Circle them in the drawing on the right.

[3] DIFFICULTY ✪✪✪✪✪✪✪☆☆☆
Target time: 5 minutes

Can you answer these questions about the puzzle on the previous page without checking back?

1. How many Ms are white?

2. How many Es are dark gray?

3. How many Hs are white?

4. How many Ks are purple?

5. How many Ks are there in total?

6. What is the total of yellow Ks plus yellow Es?

7. What is the total of blue Hs plus purple Zs?

8. What is the total of all letters except Es?

5 DIFFICULTY ✪✪☆☆☆☆☆☆☆☆
Target time: 2 minutes

Three dice were placed on a glass coffee table to amuse baby Adam, crawling underneath. Adam can see only the bottom faces of the dice. If he could count, what is the total number of spots he'd say he can see?

6 DIFFICULTY ✪✪✪✪✪✪✪☆☆☆

Target time: 30 minutes

You may want to run as far away as possible from this nonogram!

HOW TO DO A NONOGRAM:

Along each row or column, there are numbers that indicate how many blocks of black squares are in a line. For example, "3, 4, 5" indicates that from left to right or top to bottom, there is a group of three black squares, then a group of four black squares, then another group of five black squares.

Each block of black squares on the same line must have at least one white square between it and the next block of black squares. Blocks of black squares may or may not have a number of white squares before and after them.

It is sometimes possible to determine which squares will be black without reference to other lines or columns.

It is helpful to put a small dot in a square you know will be empty.

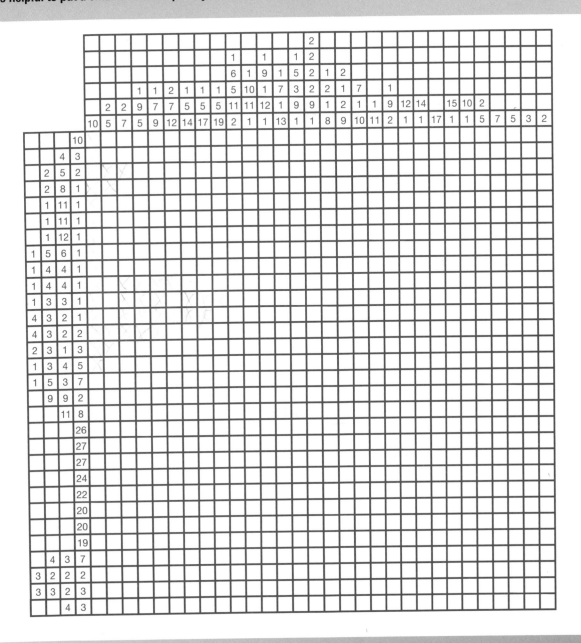

7 DIFFICULTY ★★★★★☆☆☆☆☆

Target time: 6 minutes

Find your way to the center of the maze.

8 DIFFICULTY ✪✪✪✪✩✩✩✩✩✩
Target time: 3 minutes

Which of the four boxed figures completes the set?

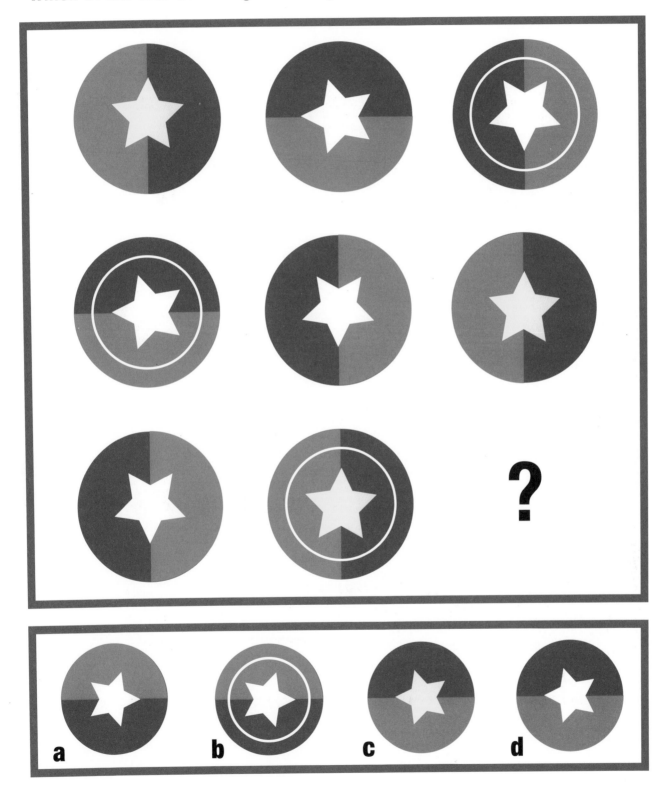

9 DIFFICULTY ★★★★★★☆☆☆
Target time: 10 minutes

There is only one place in which Pattern a can be found in the grid. The pattern may be rotated but not reflected. Can you find it? Similarly, there are three places in which Pattern b is hidden in the grid. Find them, too.

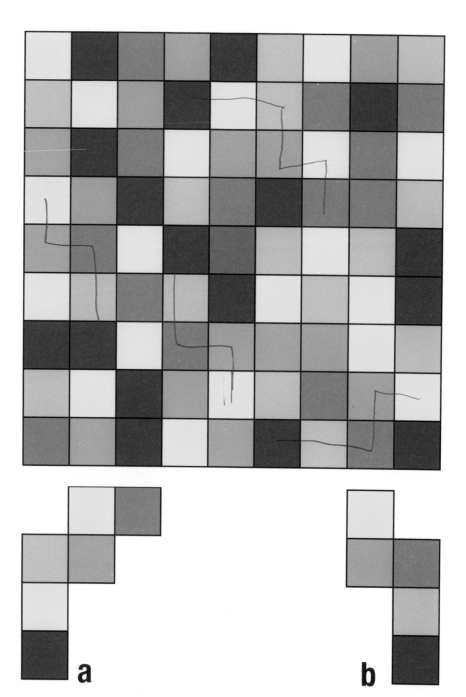

a

b

10 DIFFICULTY ✪✪✪✪☆☆☆☆☆☆

Target time: 4 minutes

Cinderella (not pictured here!) has two identical ugly stepsisters. Can you identify them? They might even be reflections of one another, so look carefully.

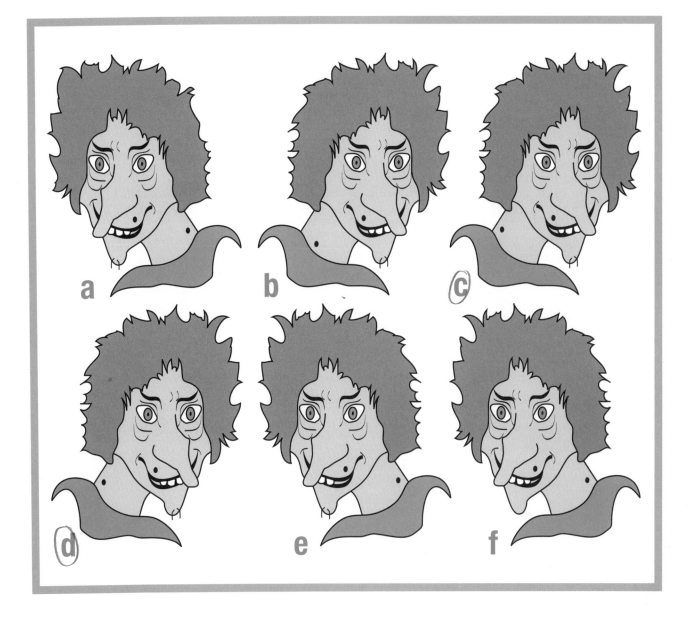

a   b   c

d   e   f

11 DIFFICULTY ✪✪✪✪☆☆☆☆☆☆
Target time: 4 minutes

When the figure below is folded to form a cube, which one of the following (a, b, c, d, or e) can be reproduced?

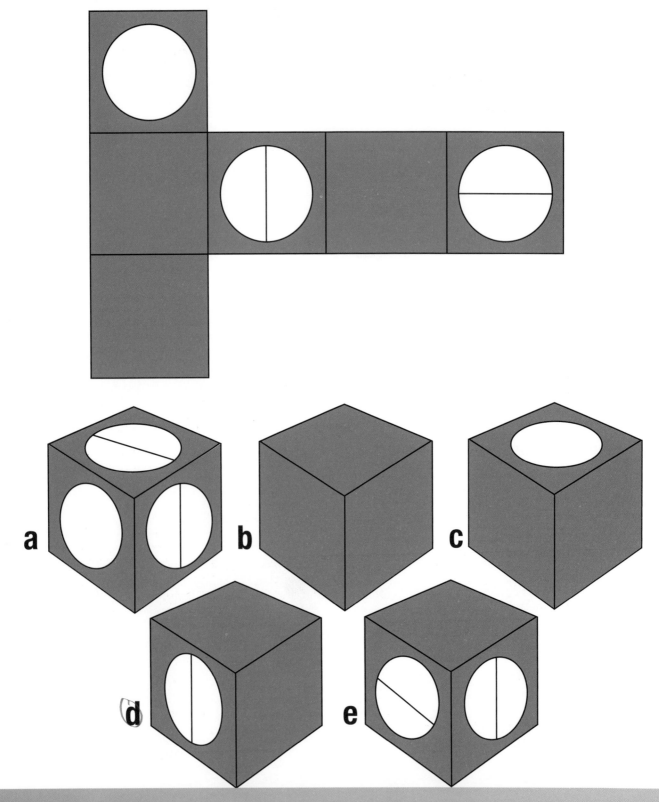

12 DIFFICULTY ⭐⭐⭐⭐⭐☆☆☆☆☆
Target time: 3 minutes

Which domino (a, b, c, or d) should fill the empty space?

a   **b**   **c**   **d**

13 DIFFICULTY ⭐⭐⭐⭐⭐⭐⭐☆☆☆
Target time: 5 minutes

Juliette has lined up these three dice on her coffee table. She can see the same seven faces that you can see. Angelica (her friend, sitting opposite) can see the top three faces of the dice, as well as a further four faces you and Juliette cannot see. None of you can see the bottom three faces of these dice. What is the total number of spots on all the faces of the dice that Angelica can see, given that there aren't six spots visible to anyone on the die furthest right from your point of view as you look at the diagram?

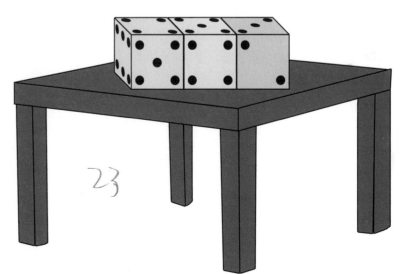

14 DIFFICULTY ★★★★★☆☆☆☆

Target time: 6 minutes

Should the central circle be a  or a ?

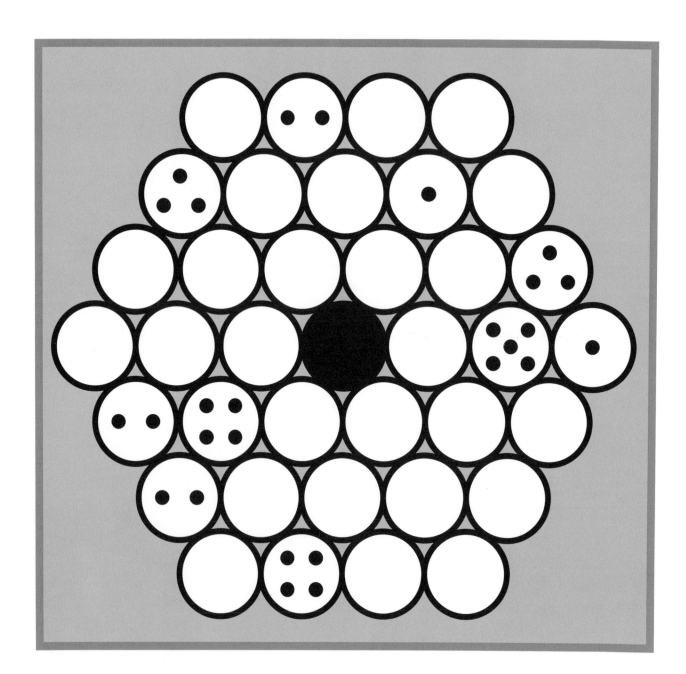

15 DIFFICULTY ✪✪✪✪☆☆☆☆☆☆
Target time: 4 minutes

Carefully study the pens below. Which is different from the rest?

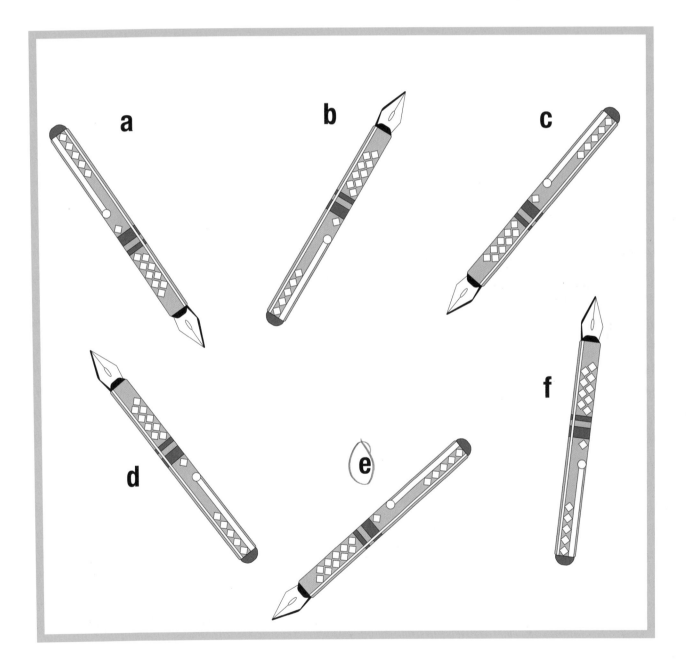

16 DIFFICULTY ⬤⬤⬤☆☆☆☆☆☆

Target time: 3 minutes

Color in the shape below. Can you find the minimum number of different colors needed so that no two touching areas are the same color?

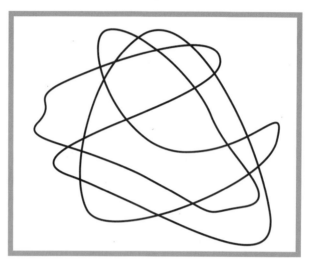

17 DIFFICULTY ⬤⬤⬤☆☆☆☆☆☆

Target time: 3 minutes

Pat the dog has laid out his bones for your inspection. Can you deduce the order in which he placed them on the pile?

18 DIFFICULTY ★★★☆☆☆☆☆☆☆

Target time: 5 minutes

Get your automobile to the garage, marked with an X, avoiding the potholes as you go.

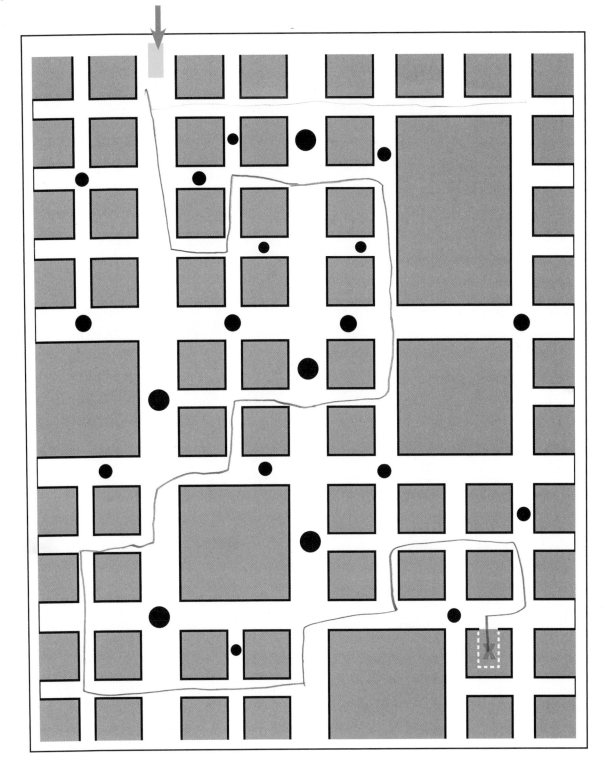

19

A tangram is an ancient Chinese puzzle. To make your own tangram, take a piece of cardboard (the thicker the better) and draw a 4 x 4 grid pattern on it. Then cut out seven pieces, as indicated by this diagram.

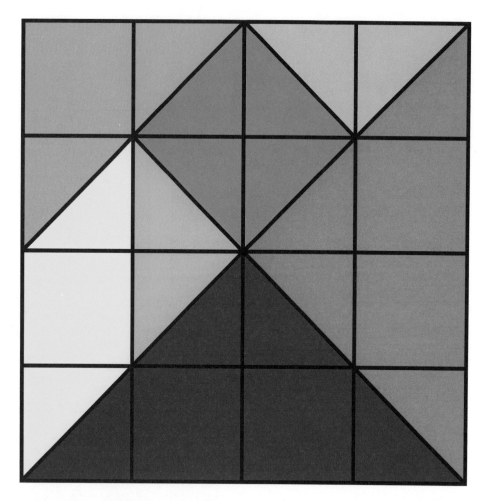

Now rearrange the shapes to make the images on the facing page. You must use all seven pieces each time, and overlapping the pieces is not allowed. We've done one for you, below.

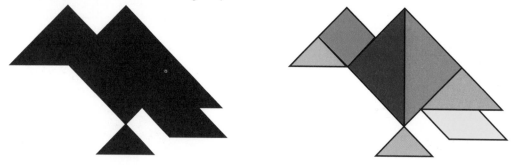

a DIFFICULTY
★★★☆☆☆☆☆☆☆
Target time: 3 minutes

Sleeping cat

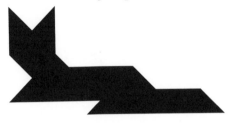

b DIFFICULTY
★★★☆☆☆☆☆☆☆
Target time: 3 minutes

Candle

c DIFFICULTY
★★★★☆☆☆☆☆☆
Target time: 5 minutes

Man in the hat

d DIFFICULTY
★★★★★☆☆☆☆☆
Target time: 5 minutes

Curious arrow

e DIFFICULTY
★★★★★★★★☆☆
Target time: 8 minutes

Paradoxical square

f DIFFICULTY
★★★★★★★★☆☆
Target time: 8 minutes

Mountains into molehills

20 DIFFICULTY ✪✪✪✪✪✪✪✪✪☆
Target time: 8 minutes

When the shape below is folded to form a cube, which one of the following (a, b, c, d, or e) can be produced?

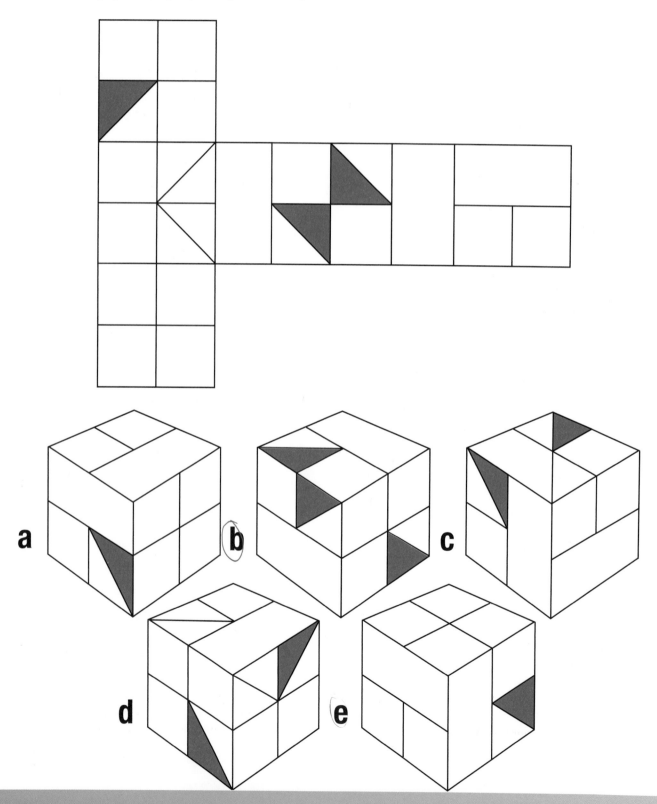

21 DIFFICULTY ★★☆☆☆☆☆☆☆☆
Target time: 2 minutes

Which of the four boxed figures at the bottom completes the set above it?

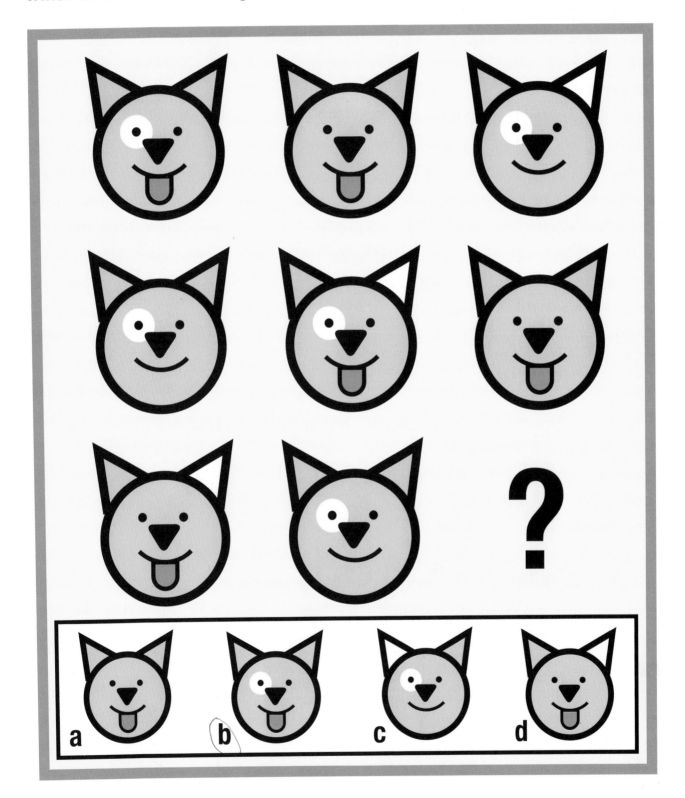

22 DIFFICULTY ✪✪✪✪✪✩✩✩✩✩

Target time: 3 minutes

Which two pieces will fit together perfectly to form a purple copy of this white shape? Pieces may be rotated, but not flipped over.

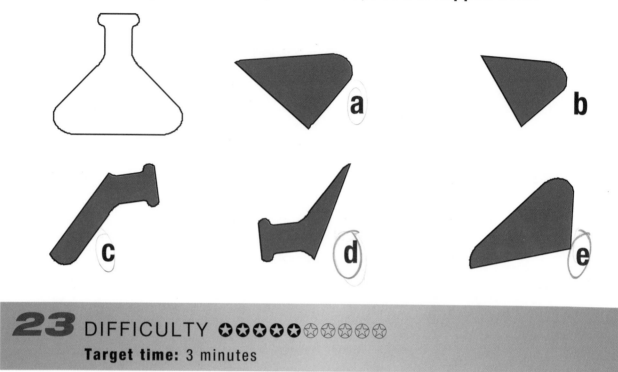

23 DIFFICULTY ✪✪✪✪✪✩✩✩✩✩

Target time: 3 minutes

Which domino (a, b, c, or d) should fill the empty space?

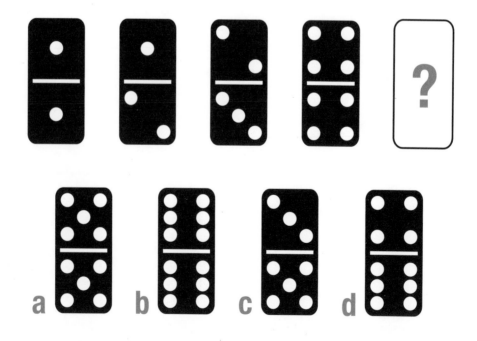

24 DIFFICULTY ✪✪✪✪✪✩✩✩✩✩

Target time: 5 minutes

Carefully study the pictures below. Which crane is different from the rest?

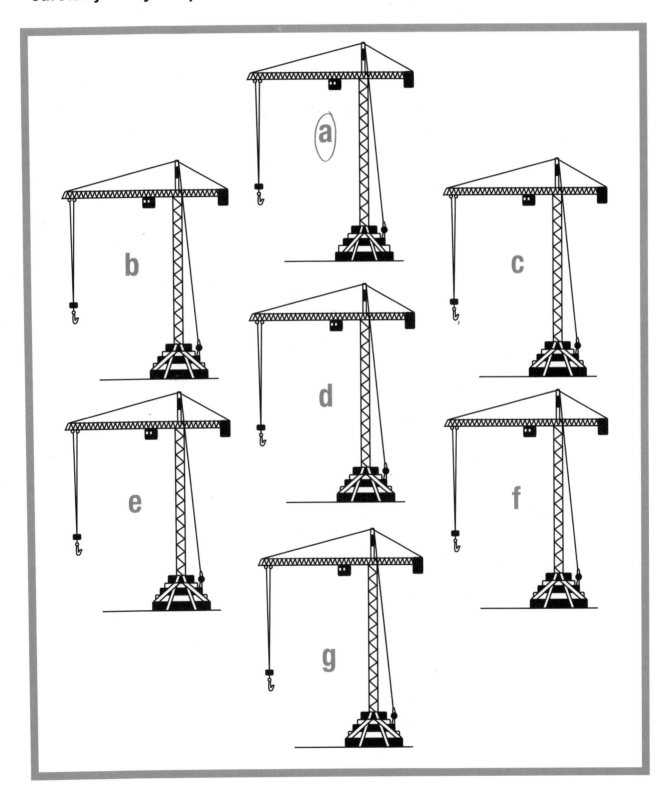

25 DIFFICULTY ✪✪✪✪✪✪✩✩✩
Target time: 7 minutes

What shape should be in the center square? (If you need a clue to help you work out the answer, the colors you see are red, blue, green, yellow, and apricot.)

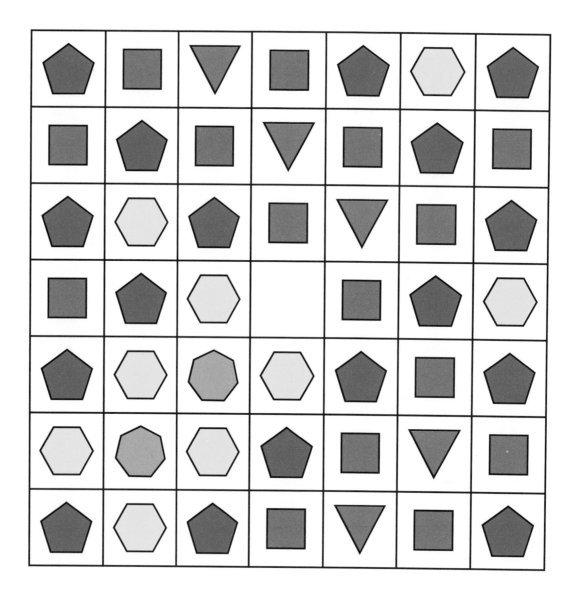

26 DIFFICULTY ●●●●●●●●●○○

Target time: 30 minutes

This nonogram is ripe for solving. (See puzzle 6 for advice on how to complete a nonogram.)

Column clues (columns 1–30, read top to bottom):

																			3							2	2	1	
						1										2	1	3	2	2	2				3	2	2	2	
				3	2	4	5	2	1			3			2	2	3	4	2	2	2	1		1	1	2	3	3	3
	3	3	3	4	4	3	3	3	3		3	1	2	3	1	7	4	3	3	3	3	3		3	2	3	3	2	6
4	1	2	3	4	8	4	7	8	10	18	15	15	13	12	10	4	8	4	7	8	10	16	30	15	13	12	10	7	4

Row clues (rows 1–30, read left to right):

		4	1	2	1	1	3
3	2	1	2	2	1	2	1
3	4	2	2	3	1	1	2
3	3	2	2	3	1	1	2
			3	4	8	1	3
				2	4	1	6
			1	4	4	2	1
				5	6	2	2
					8	2	3
				3	6	1	4
			3	6	3	1	3
			2	8	2	2	3
				2	10	3	3
				2	11	4	2
			2	11	2	2	1
					14	4	4
					12	6	3
					12	8	1
					10	3	6
					8	3	6
					4	2	8
						2	10
						2	11
						2	11
							14
							12
							12
							10
							8
							4

27 DIFFICULTY ✪✪✪✪☆☆☆☆☆☆
Target time: 5 minutes

Divide this picture by drawing three straight lines to produce five sections, each containing five different shapes in five different colors.

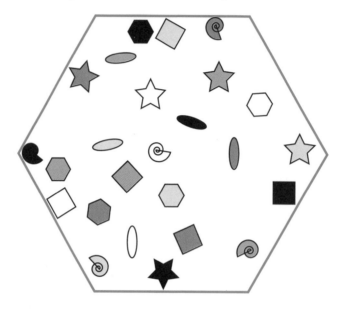

28 DIFFICULTY ✪✪✪✪✪☆☆☆☆☆
Target time: 5 minutes

What is the minimum number of different colors needed to color in this honeycomb pattern (including the background) in such a way that no two touching areas are the same color?

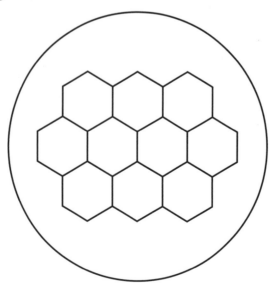

29 DIFFICULTY ✪✪✪✪✩✩✩✩✩✪
Target time: 4 minutes

Maggie's magic mirror reflects very strangely! Can you match each jug to its correct (although misplaced and somewhat distorted) image in the mirror on the right?

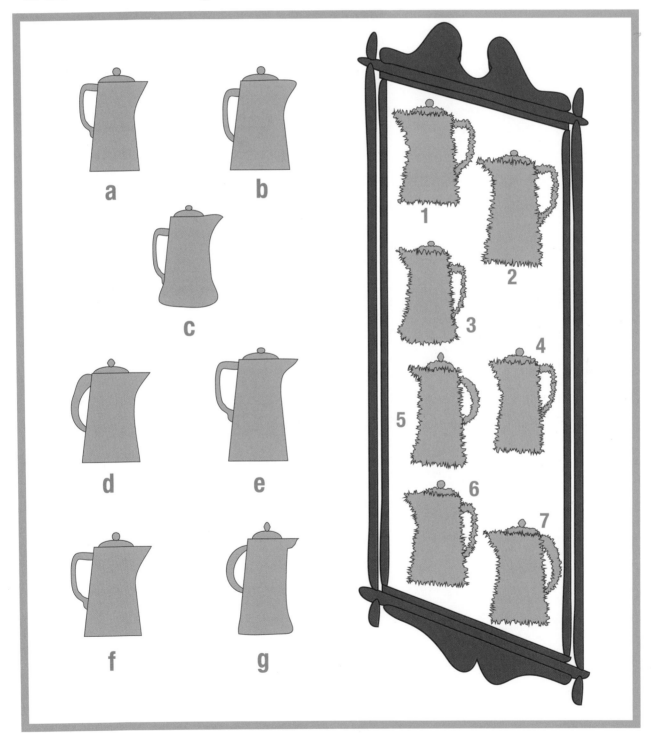

30 DIFFICULTY ✪✪✪✪✪✪✪✪✩
Target time: 8 minutes

Dominoes can be arranged into square "picture frames"—this example shows such a frame, where every side adds up to eighteen.

Can you arrange the eight dominoes below into two square frames, each made of four pieces, so that all the sides of both frames add up to nine?

31 DIFFICULTY ✪✪✪✪✪✪✪✩✩✩
Target time: 7 minutes

Divide this picture by drawing two straight lines to produce three sections, each containing two butterflies, four caterpillars, and five larvae.

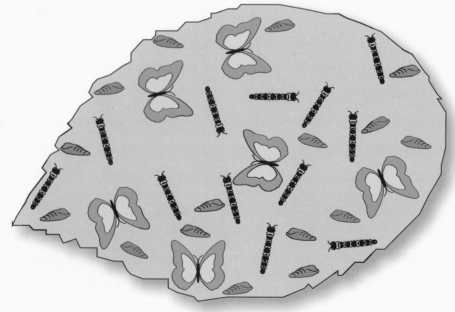

32 DIFFICULTY ✪✪✪✪✪✪✪☆☆☆
Target time: 5 minutes

Study these cupcakes for one minute, then see if you can answer the questions on the next page without checking back.

[32] DIFFICULTY ✪✪✪✪✪✪✪☆☆☆
Target time: 5 minutes

Can you answer these questions about the puzzle on the previous page without checking back?

1. What color is the frosting on cupcake c?

2. What color is the case containing cupcake g?

3. How many cupcake cases are blue?

4. How many plates have blue trim?

5. How many of the cherries on cupcake f have a leaf?

6. How many cupcakes are in white cases?

7. How many cupcakes have white frosting?

8. How many cherries does cupcake e have?

33 DIFFICULTY ✪✪✪✪✪☆☆☆☆☆
Target time: 5 minutes

Can you spot the eight differences between these two pictures? Circle them in the drawing on the right.

34 DIFFICULTY ✪✪✪✪✩✩✩✩✩✩
Target time: 3 minutes

Which of the four boxed figures at the bottom completes the set?

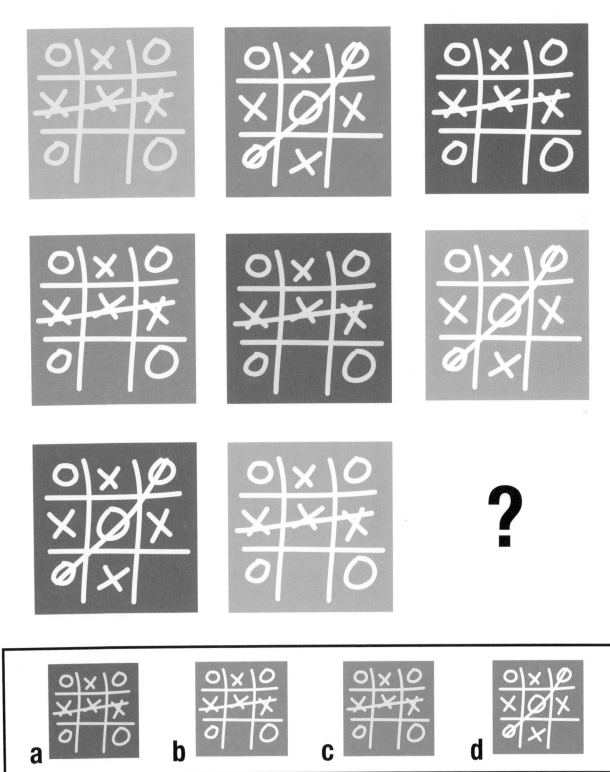

a   b   c   d

35 DIFFICULTY ✪✪✪✪✪☆☆☆☆☆

Target time: 5 minutes

When the shape below is folded to form a cube, which one of the following (a, b, c, d, or e) can be produced?

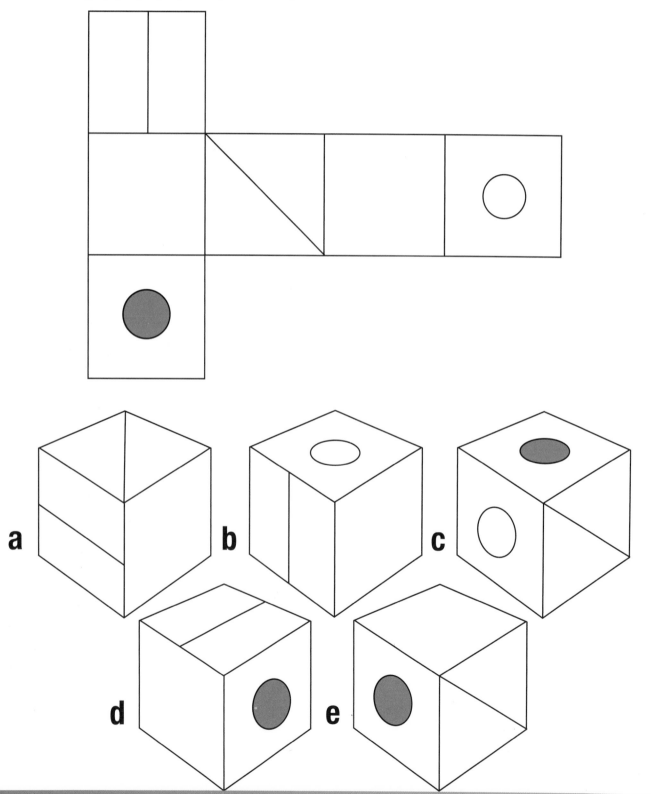

36 DIFFICULTY ✪✪✪✪✩✩✩✩✩
Target time: 3 minutes

Which two pieces will fit together perfectly to form a green copy of this white shape? Pieces may be rotated, but not flipped over.

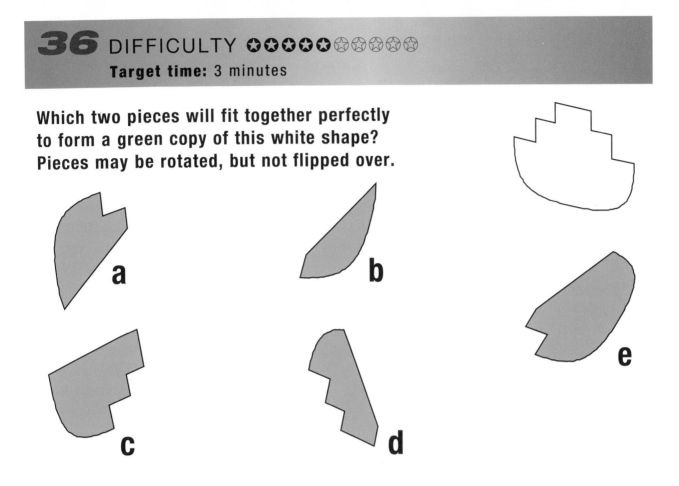

37 DIFFICULTY ✪✪✪✪✩✩✩✩✩
Target time: 5 minutes

Starting with the top row of coins, move any two adjacent coins four times, separating the heads from the tails, to end up with the bottom row.

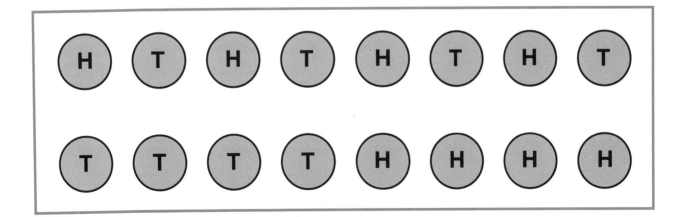

38 DIFFICULTY ✪✪✪✪✪✪✪✪✪✩
Target time: 10 minutes

The square below contains exactly one of each of thirty-six faces from six standard dice. In each horizontal row of six smaller squares, each vertical column of six smaller squares, and both diagonal lines of six smaller squares, there are faces with different numbers of spots.

We've placed a few to give you a start, but can you provide the rest using only the given clues?

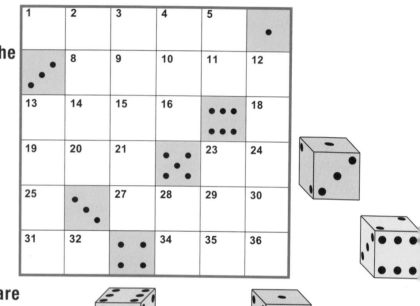

1. The face of the die in square 3 has the same number of spots as that in square 32.
2. The face of the die in square 14 has the same number of spots as that in square 31.
3. The face of the die in square 25 has the same number of spots as that in square 36.

39 DIFFICULTY ✪✪✪✪✪✪✪✪✩✩
Target time: 5 minutes

Here are five clocks. Four are perfect, but the fifth was damaged. Can you determine the time on clock e?

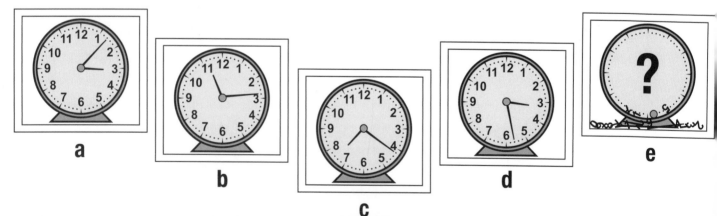

a   b   c   d   e

40 DIFFICULTY ✪✪✪✪✪✪✪☆☆☆
Target time: 7 minutes

Carefully study the diagrams below. Which is different from the rest?

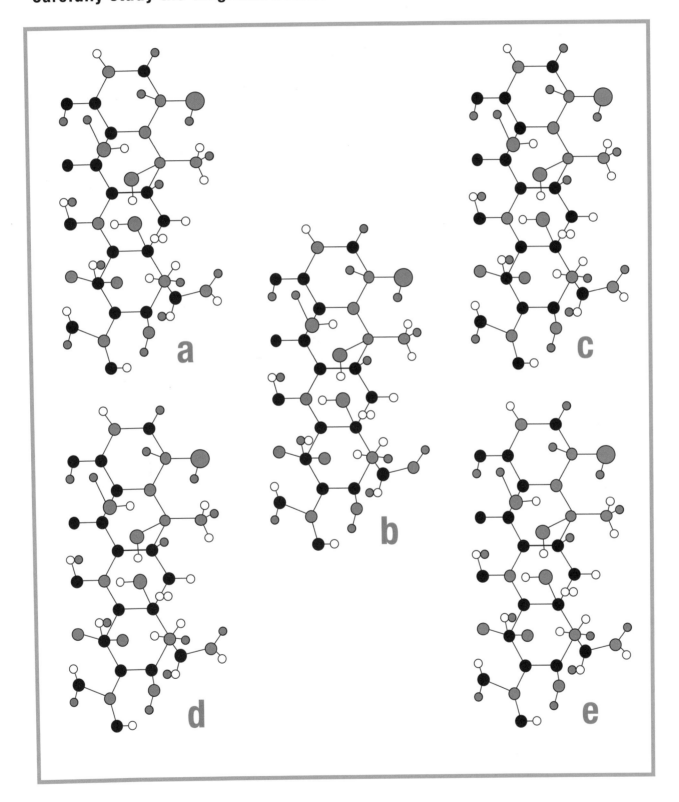

41 DIFFICULTY ★★★★★☆☆☆☆☆
Target time: 6 minutes

Find your way through the woods from the cabin at the top to the picnic table marked with an X.

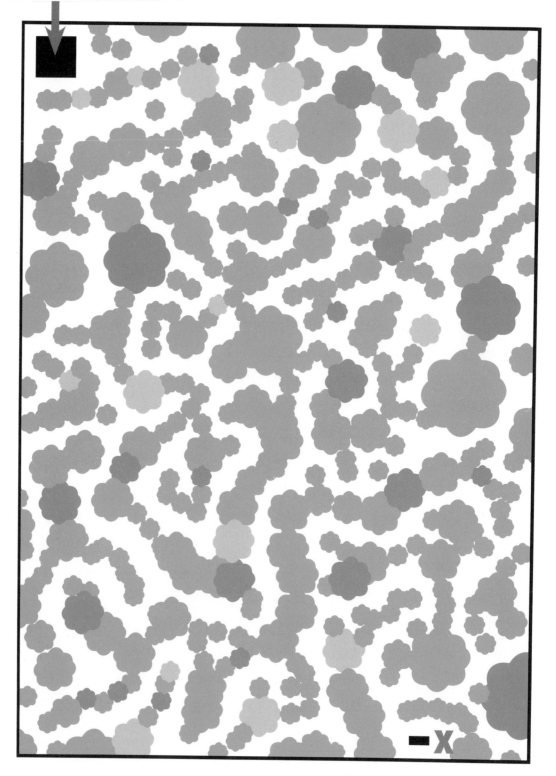

42 DIFFICULTY ✪✪✪✪✪✩✩✩✩✩
Target time: 6 minutes

Find a route from the top to the bottom down through the pipes, avoiding any blockages.

43 DIFFICULTY ✪✪✪✪✪✩✩✩✩✩
Target time: 5 minutes

Can you deduce the minimum number of different colors needed to color in the diagram in such a way that no two touching areas are the same?

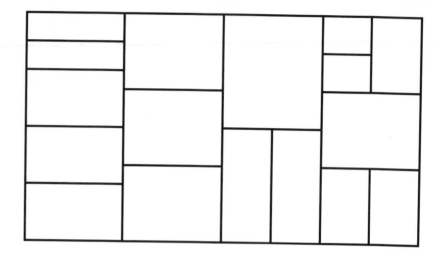

44 DIFFICULTY ✪✪✪✪✪✪✪✪✪✪
Target time: 10 minutes

The square below contains one of each of thirty-six faces from six standard dice. In each horizontal row of six smaller squares and each vertical column of six smaller squares, there are faces with different numbers of spots. Also in the long diagonal line of six smaller squares from top left to bottom right, there are faces with different numbers of spots. In the long diagonal line from top right to bottom left, however, no face has four spots, but there are faces with five different numbers. We've placed a few to give you a start. Given that the total number of spots on the four corner dice equals fourteen, can you place the rest?

45 DIFFICULTY ✪✪✪✪✪✪✪✩✩
Target time: 12 minutes

1. There is only one place in which Pattern a can be found in the grid. The pattern may be rotated but not reflected. Can you find it?
2. Similarly, there are six places in which Pattern b is hidden in the grid. Can you find them?

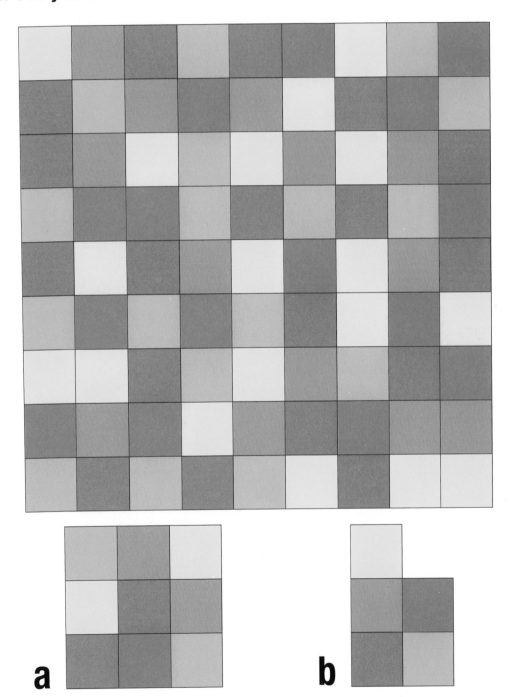

a

b

46 DIFFICULTY ★★★☆☆☆☆☆☆☆
Target time: 3 minutes

Can you spot the six differences between these two pictures?
Circle them in the drawing on the right.

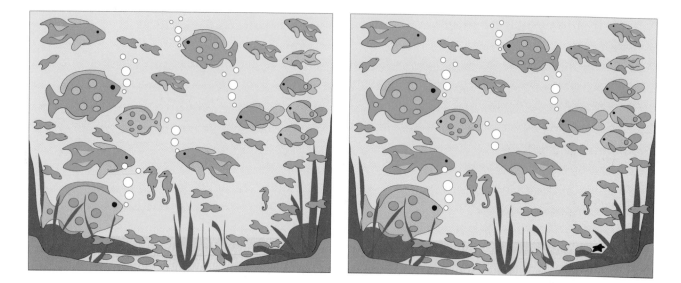

47 DIFFICULTY ★★★★★★☆☆☆☆
Target time: 6 minutes

Can you divide this square on the right into four identical shapes, each composed of sixteen smaller squares, and each containing four different shapes?

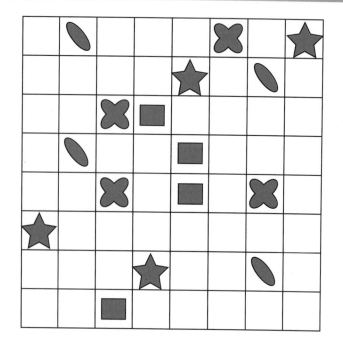

48 DIFFICULTY ✪✪✪✪✪✪✪✪✪✪

Target time: 3 minutes

Which two pieces will fit together perfectly to form a red copy of this white star? Pieces may be rotated, but not flipped over.

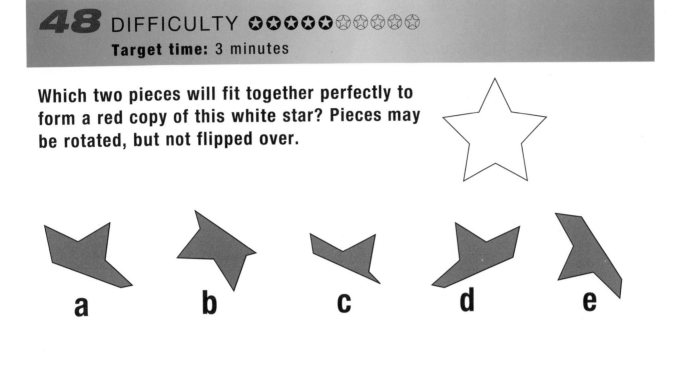

49 DIFFICULTY ✪✪✪✪✪✪✪✪✪✪

Target time: 6 minutes

Dominoes can be arranged into square picture frames. This example shows a frame where every side adds up to eighteen. Can you arrange the eight dominoes below into two square frames made of four pieces each, so that all the sides of both frames add up to ten?

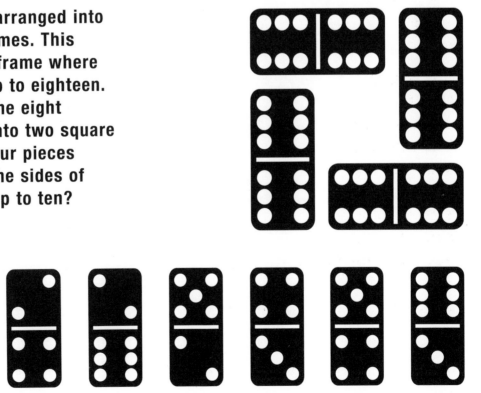

50 DIFFICULTY ★★★★★☆☆☆☆
Target time: 6 minutes

Slide one of the dominoes marked by an arrow into the center to complete the hidden pattern. Which one of the four should it be?

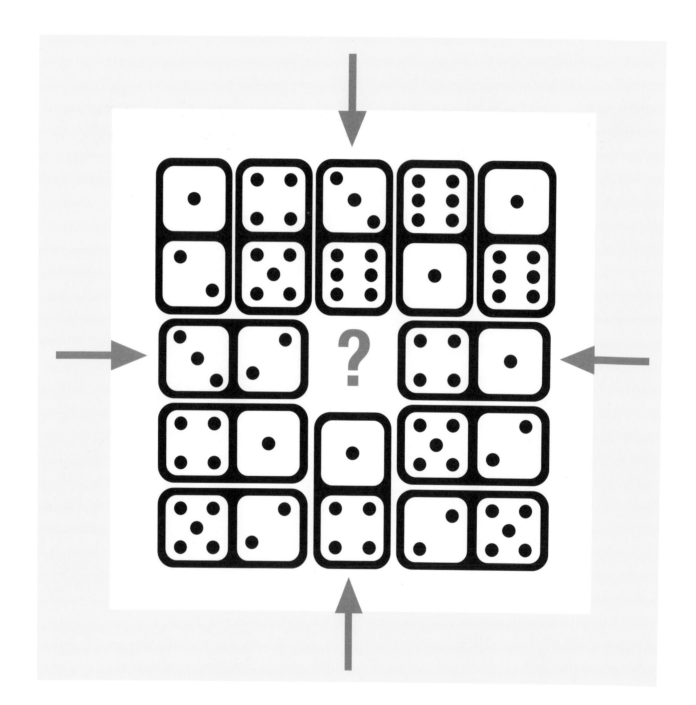

51 DIFFICULTY ✪✪✪✪✪✪✩✩✩
Target time: 7 minutes

Only two of these vases of flowers are the same. Can you identify them?
They might even be reflections of one another, so look closely!

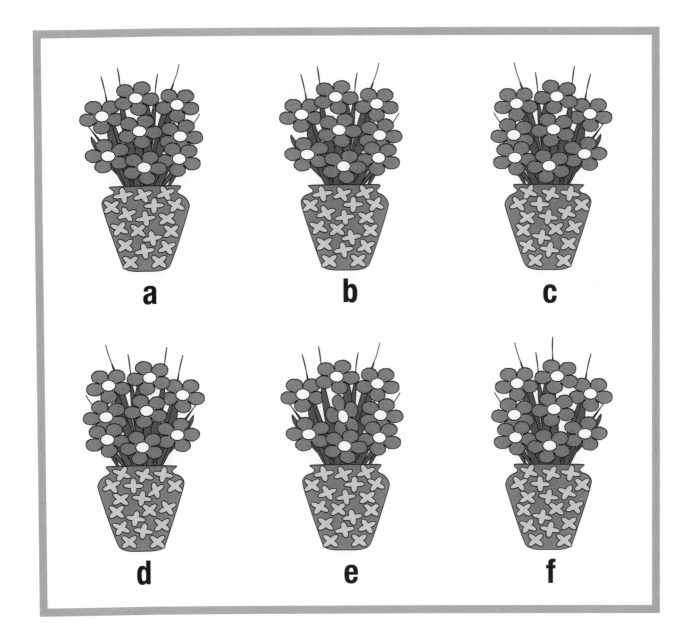

a

b

c

d

e

f

52 DIFFICULTY ✪✪✪✪✪✪✪✪✪✪

Target time: 15 minutes

This is a one-player solitaire game. Place four silver coins on spaces 1 to 4, and four pennies on spaces 5 to 8. The aim is to make the coins swap sides by sliding them from circle to circle. Only one coin per space is allowed, and coins must not jump one another.

How many moves are there in the shortest solution? One move counts as sliding one coin from one space to another in a straight line, moving through any number of unoccupied spaces along the way.

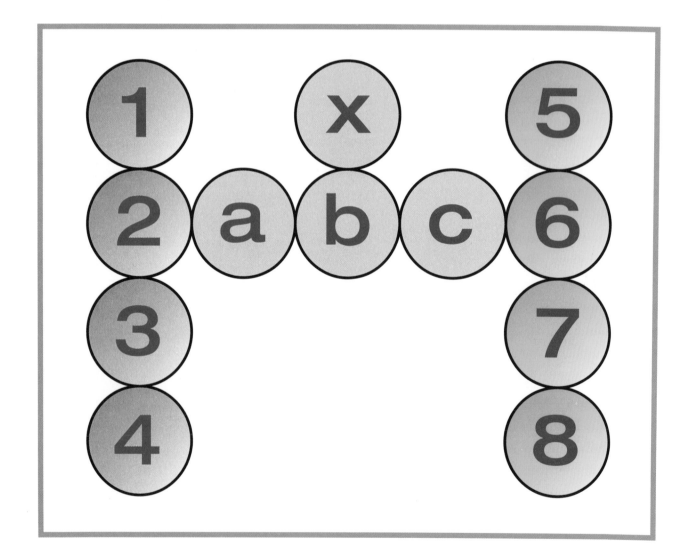

53 DIFFICULTY ★★★★★★☆☆☆
Target time: 30 minutes

Don't be scared by this nonogram! (See puzzle 6 for advice on how to complete a nonogram.)

Column clues (top):

								1																					
						1	1	3																					
						1	3	1																					
					4	2	2	4				1		1														
	4	3	2	2	4	5	4	2	6			1		2	1		1											
	1	2	2	3	2	1	1	3	2			6		2	1	2	1	1	2	2	2	2	4	4	5	7	12	
10	6	5	4	5	4	3	1	2	3	1	7	7	19	12	4	9	2	8	4	2	1	4	3	1	2	1	1	1
11	9	10	2	2	2	1	1	1	1	1	1	16	1	1	12	1	13	1	1	2	1	1	1	2	2	3	7	11

Row clues (left):

			11	11
			8	8
	5	3	5
4	1	2	5
	3	4	3
2	5	2	2
	1	8	2
	1	5	1
	1	6	1
	1	7	1
	2	3	1
	1	1	1
			7
			12
		8	3
4	7	2	5
	5	8	4
		6	13
		6	10
	1	10	1
	1	17	1
	8	8	1
	7	9	1
	6	9	2
3 1 3	1	1	2
	3 3	1	1	2
	3	2	2	2
3 1	3	3	3
		6	6
		11	9

54 DIFFICULTY ★★★★★☆☆☆☆

Target time: 6 minutes

In the sequence below, which of the lettered alternatives (a, b, c, or d) should replace the question mark?

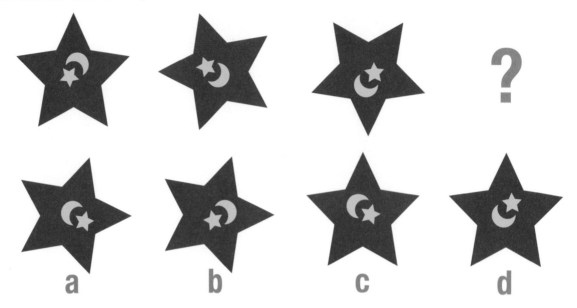

55 DIFFICULTY ★★★★★★☆☆☆☆

Target time: 6 minutes

Can you spot the eight differences between these two pictures? Circle them in the drawing on the right.

56 DIFFICULTY ⭐⭐⭐☆☆☆☆☆☆☆
Target time: 2 minutes

Which domino (a, b, c, or d) should fill the empty space?

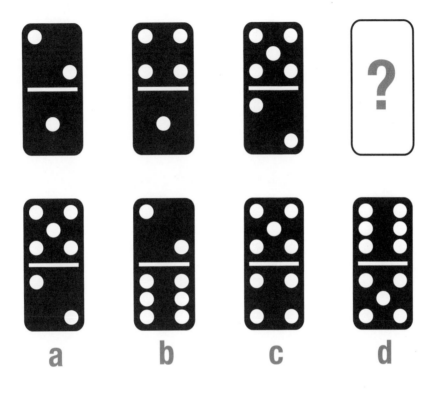

57 DIFFICULTY ⭐⭐⭐⭐⭐⭐⭐☆☆☆
Target time: 5 minutes

You may well need a break after decid-ing which two pieces fit together perfectly to form a mirror image copy of this teacup. Pieces may be rotated, but not flipped over.

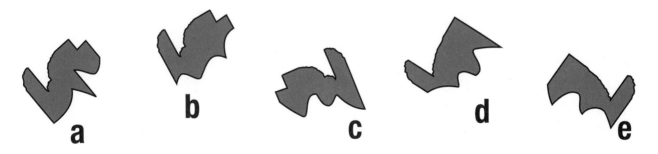

58 DIFFICULTY ★★★★★★☆☆☆
Target time: 7 minutes

At first glance, these diggers may look the same, but only two are identical. They might even be reflections of one another. How quickly can you decide which two are the same?

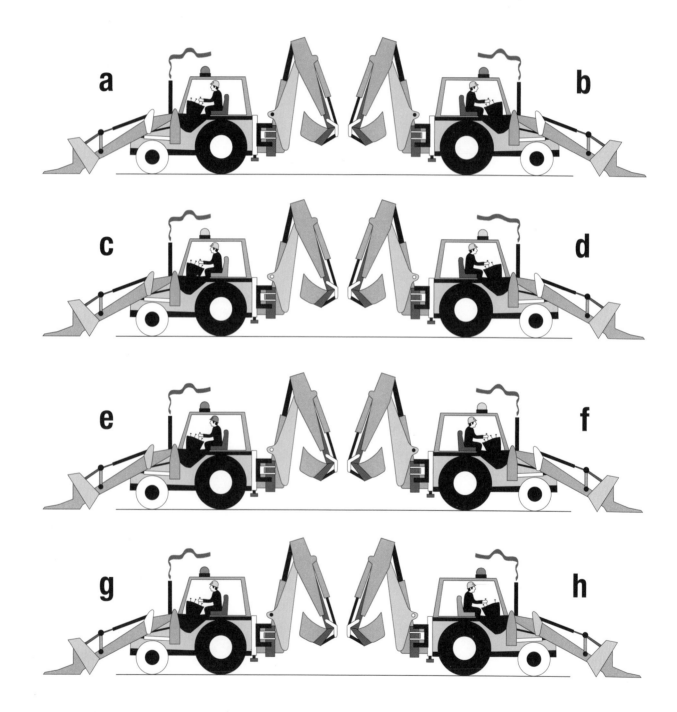

59 DIFFICULTY ★★★★★☆☆☆☆☆
Target time: 4 minutes

Which of the four boxed figures (a, b, c, or d) completes the set?

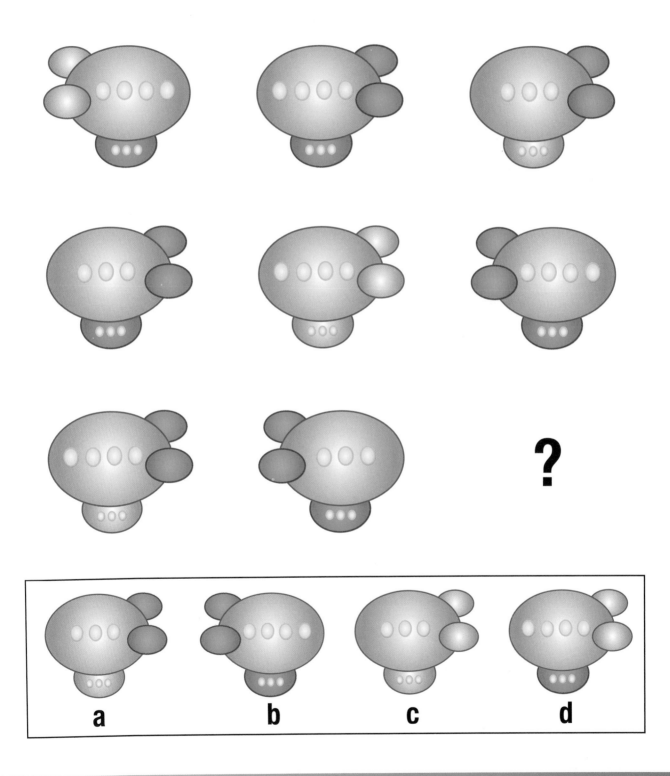

a   b   c   d

MINDW⚙RKS BRAIN TRAINING

60 DIFFICULTY ★★★★★☆☆☆☆
Target time: 5 minutes

Change all the rows either to all heads or all tails, without touching more than ONE coin.

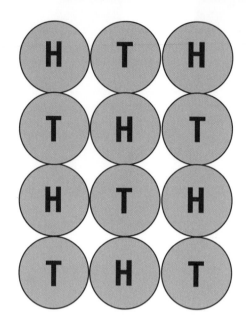

61 DIFFICULTY ★★★★★★☆☆☆
Target time: 7 minutes

Can you divide this square into four identical shapes, each composed of sixteen squares, and each containing five different chess pieces?

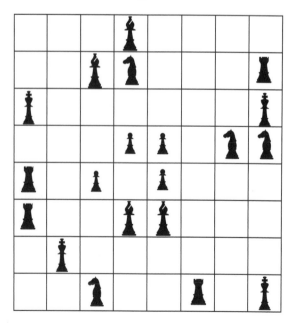

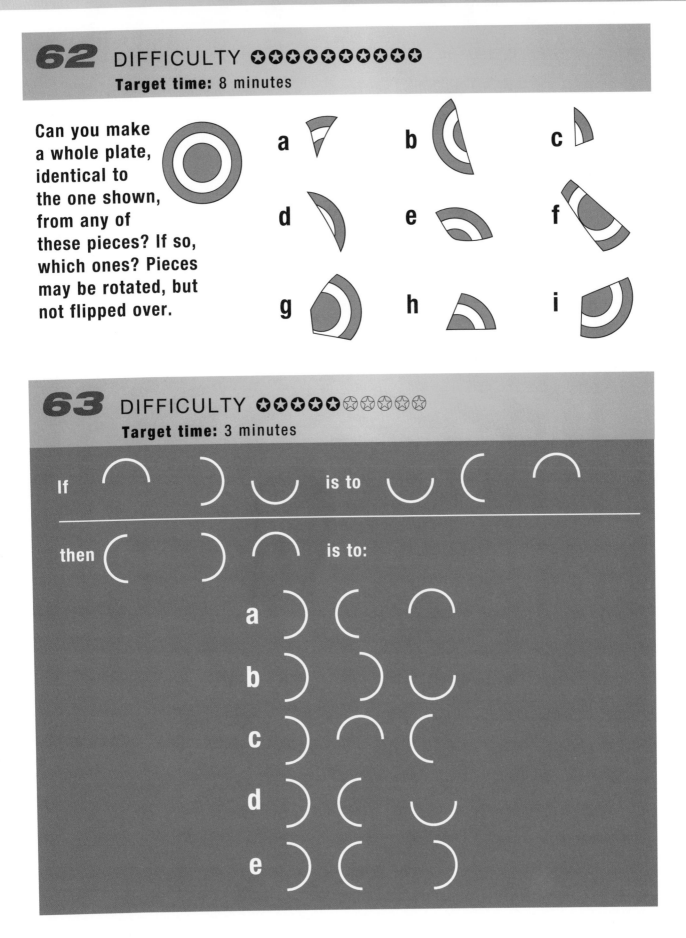

62 DIFFICULTY ✪✪✪✪✪✪✪✪✪✪
Target time: 8 minutes

Can you make a whole plate, identical to the one shown, from any of these pieces? If so, which ones? Pieces may be rotated, but not flipped over.

a
b
c
d
e
f
g
h
i

63 DIFFICULTY ✪✪✪✪✪☆☆☆☆☆
Target time: 3 minutes

If ⌒ ⌣ ⌣ is to ⊃⊂ ⌒

then ⊃ ⌒ is to:

a

b

c

d

e

64 DIFFICULTY ★★★★★☆☆☆☆☆
Target time: 6 minutes

Find your way through the maze. X marks the exit.

65 DIFFICULTY ✪✪✪✪✪✪✪☆☆
Target time: 6 minutes

Study these nine sets of chairs, lamps, and tables for one minute, then see if you can answer the questions on the next page.

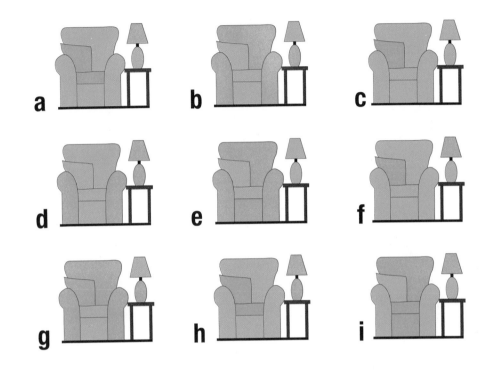

66 DIFFICULTY ✪✪✪✪✪☆☆☆☆☆
Target time: 5 minutes

Can you spot the eight differences between these two pictures? Circle them in the picture on the right.

[65] DIFFICULTY ✪✪✪✪✪✪✪☆☆
Target time: 6 minutes

Can you answer these questions about the puzzle on the previous page without checking back?

1. What color is the cushion on chair f?

2. What color are the arms of chair g?

3. How many lamps have both an orange shade and an orange base?

4. How many chairs have both a green cushion and a green seat?

5. How many chairs have both an orange back and a green seat?

6. How many lamps have both a green shade and a green base?

7. How many lamps have both an orange shade and a green base?

8. What color is the shade on the lamp next to chair h?

67 DIFFICULTY ✪✪✪✪✪✪✪✪☆
Target time: 8 minutes

Ten dominoes have been used to build this wall, but seven have been masked out. Can you place the missing dominoes in the correct places, bearing in mind that each vertical line of four numbers (as well as the two end vertical lines of two numbers) adds up to ten; the second horizontal row of dominoes has dots totaling sixteen, and the third horizontal row of dominoes has dots totaling ten?

68 DIFFICULTY ✪✪✪✪✰✰✰✰✰
Target time: 4 minutes

Carefully study the clowns below. Which one is different from the rest?

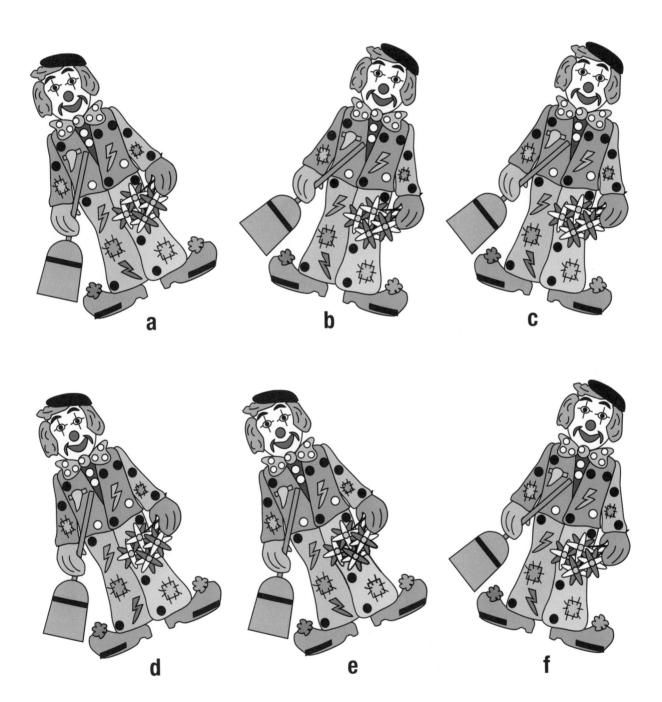

a

b

c

d

e

f

69 DIFFICULTY ⚝⚝⚝⚝☆☆☆☆☆
Target time: 4 minutes

When the shape below is folded to form a cube, which one of the following (a, b, c, d, or e) is produced?

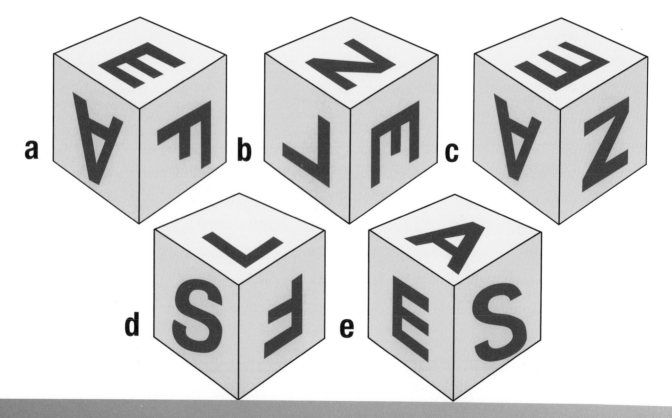

70 DIFFICULTY ✪✪✪✪✪✪☆☆☆☆

Target time: 6 minutes

Place the pieces from a standard set of twenty-eight dominoes into the following grid by matching their numbers with those in the rectangle. It's trickier than you might think, so we've placed one in position and supplied a checklist, which may help!

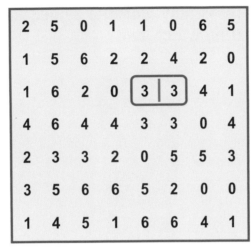

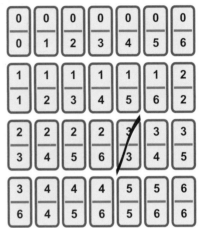

71 DIFFICULTY ✪✪✪✪✪☆☆☆☆☆

Target time: 4 minutes

Match the arrow flights with the correct arrowheads. If you pick the correct five, a name will be spelled out.

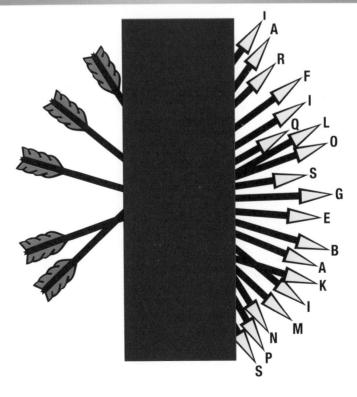

72 DIFFICULTY ✪✪✪✪✪✪☆☆☆
Target time: 7 minutes

At first glance, these dresses may look the same, but only two are identical. Can you determine which two?

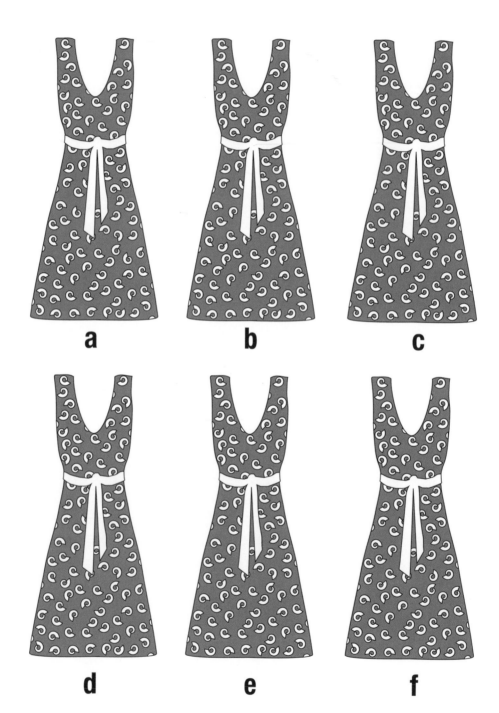

a   b   c

d   e   f

73 DIFFICULTY ✪✪✪✰✰✰✰✰✰✰
Target time: 2 minutes

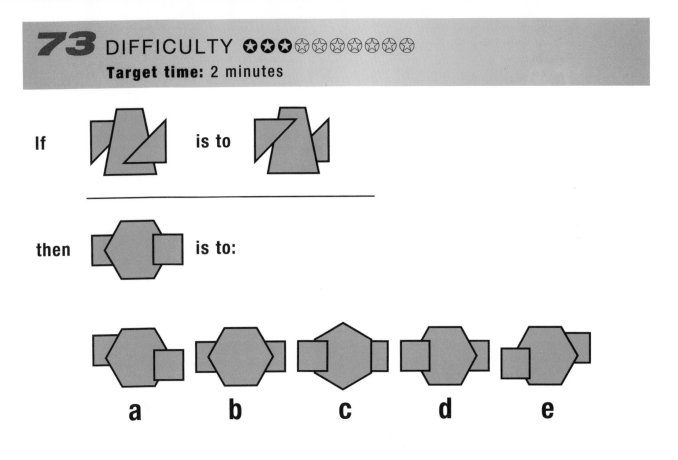

If [shape] is to [shape]

then [shape] is to:

a   b   c   d   e

74 DIFFICULTY ✪✪✪✪✪✰✰✰✰✰
Target time: 5 minutes

Can you color in this simplified version of a map of the U.S. so that no two touching areas are the same, using just four colors? You may use colored pens.

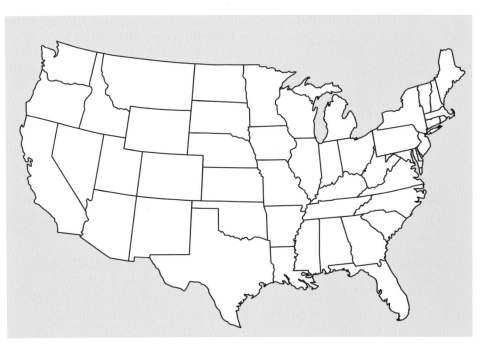

75 DIFFICULTY ★★★★★★☆☆☆☆
Target time: 4 minutes

Which of the four boxed figures (a, b, c, or d) completes the set?

76 DIFFICULTY ●●●●●●●○○○

Target time: 30 minutes

A little bird has told us that this nonogram is waiting to be solved. (See puzzle 6 for advice on how to complete a nonogram.)

						2		3																					
				2	2	1	2	4	4		15																		
				2	3	1	2	2	7	14	1	11	11	11								3	3	2					
1	2	2	2	6	3	2	2	2	3	2	2	3	2	1	12	12				6	4	2	2	2	1				
22	17	12	9	5	4	4	5	2	3	4	2	2	2	3	2	1	13	13	14	7	8	5	2	2	1	1	2	2	1

				5
				7
			1	4
		4	1	3
			3	2
			1	2
			1	4
			1	8
			1	11
		1	2	9
		1	1	10
		1	1	10
		1	1	11
		2	1	11
		2	2	12
		2	1	13
		2	2	14
		2	2	13
	3	2	6	3
		3	12	6
3	2	2	5	3
	4	2	2	6
	4	2	2	8
4	2	2	3	4
			15	3
			13	4
			8	3
			6	3
			5	4
		4	1	1

77 DIFFICULTY ✪✪✪✪✪✪✪☆☆☆
Target time: 5 minutes

Peter enjoys selling his wares at the local market on Saturdays. One day he decided to play a little game with his regular customers. Five customers agreed to play and each threw two dice. Their throws and rewards are shown on the right—except Mary's, where you can see only the dice she threw. Can you determine exactly how Peter determined how many loaves and fish each customer should get, and precisely what quantity of loaves and fish he awarded to Mary?

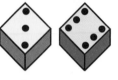

Andrew
= 8 loaves
and 2 fish

John
= 4 loaves
and 2 fish

Elizabeth
= 6 loaves
and 12 fish

James
= 8 loaves
and 6 fish

Mary
= ? loaves
and ? fish

78 DIFFICULTY ✪✪✪✪✪✪✪☆☆☆
Target time: 5 minutes

Can you spot the eight differences between these two pictures? Circle them in the drawing on the right.

79 DIFFICULTY ✪✪✪✪✪✪✪☆☆☆
Target time: 5 minutes

A table has been set for a children's party. Study the seating plan for one minute, then see if you can answer the questions on the next page without checking back.

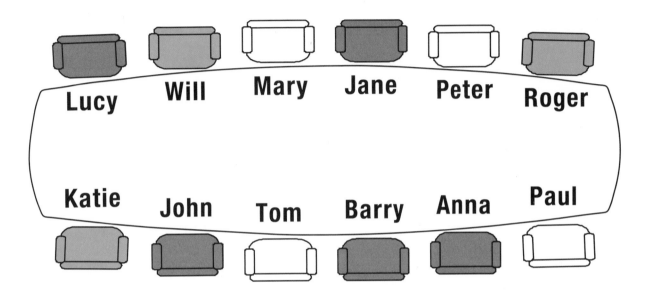

80 DIFFICULTY ✪✪✪✪✪✪✪☆☆☆
Target time: 5 minutes

Study these vases of flowers for one minute, then see if you can answer the questions on the next page without checking back.

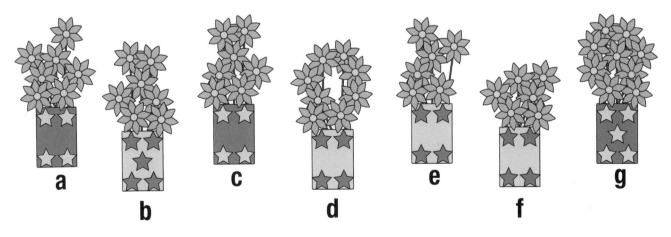

[79] DIFFICULTY ⭐⭐⭐⭐⭐☆☆☆☆☆
Target time: 5 minutes

Can you answer these questions about the puzzle on the previous page (top) without checking back?

1. Who will sit between Tom and Anna?

2. Who will sit directly opposite Paul?

3. Which boy has the shortest name?

4. What color is Mary's seat?

5. How many chairs are red?

6. How many chairs are white?

7. How many children have names ending in a, e, i, o, or u?

8. How many children will sit directly between (and on the same side of the table as) Lucy and Peter?

[80] DIFFICULTY ⭐⭐⭐⭐⭐☆☆☆☆☆
Target time: 5 minutes

Can you answer these questions about the puzzle on the previous page (bottom) without checking back?

1. Which two vases have six flowers each?

2. Which vase has the greatest number of flowers?

3. How many vases are green with yellow stars?

4. How many green vases have five yellow stars?

5. How many yellow vases hold seven flowers?

6. How many petals does each flower have?

7. How many vases have eight flowers each?

8. What is the total number of stars on all of the vases combined?

81 DIFFICULTY ✪✪✪✪✪✪✪☆☆
Target time: 8 minutes

Find a route from left to right through the maze.

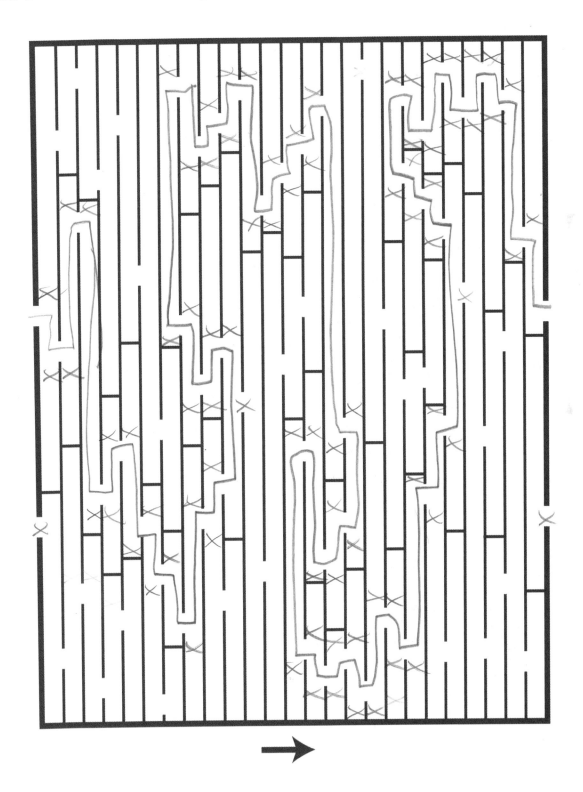

82 DIFFICULTY ✪✪✪✪✪✪✪✪✪✰
Target time: 12 minutes

How many times can you find Pattern a in the hexagonal grid? The pattern may be rotated but not reflected. Pattern b can be found in only one place in the grid. Can you find it?

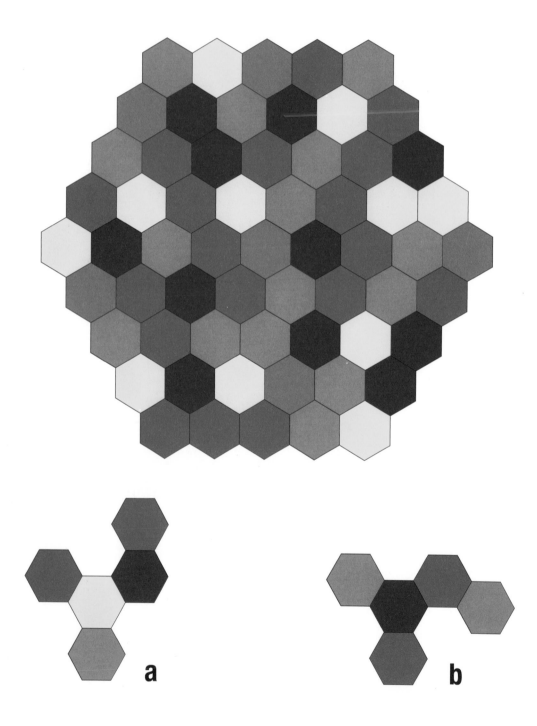

a

b

83 DIFFICULTY ✪✪✪✪✪✪✩✩✩
Target time: 7 minutes

One of these piles of mail differs in some way from the others—which is it?

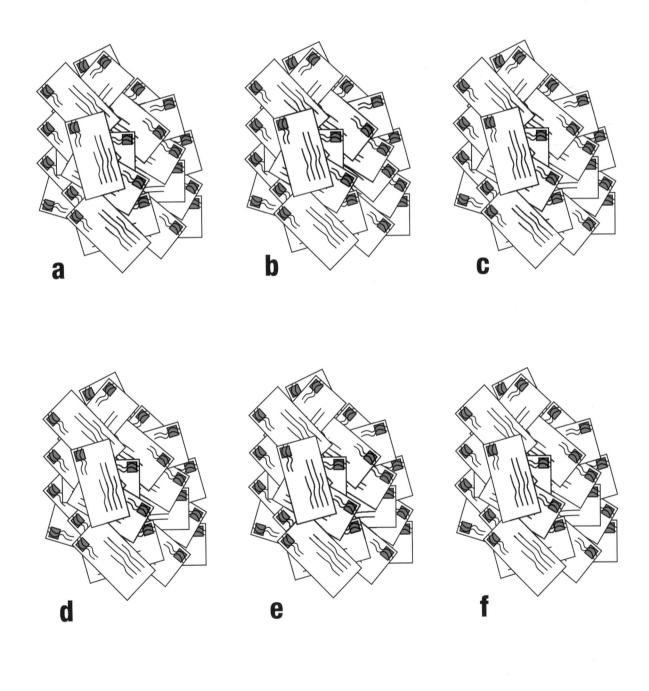

a

b

c

d

e

f

84 DIFFICULTY ✪✪✪✪✪✪✪☆☆
Target time: 30 minutes

Aren't you just burning with curiosity to find the solution to this nonogram? (See puzzle 6 for advice on how to complete a nonogram.)

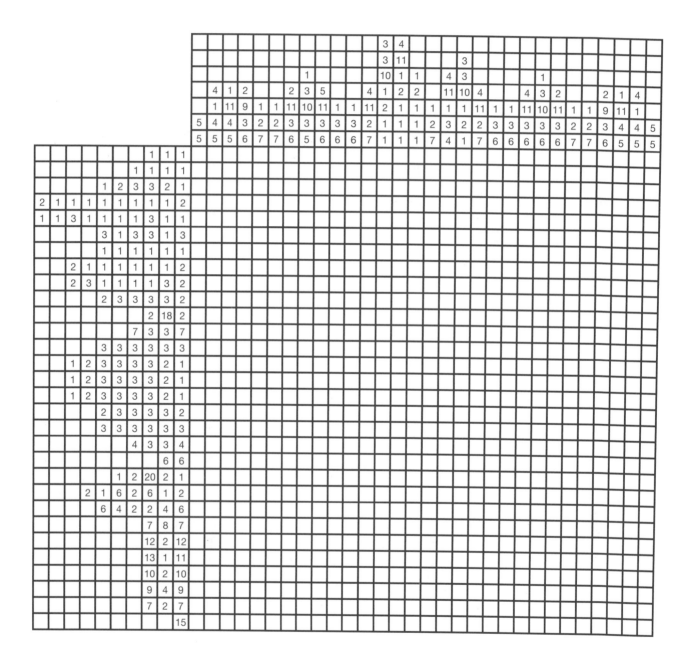

85 DIFFICULTY ✪✪✪✪✪✪☆☆☆☆
Target time: 5 minutes

When the shape below is folded to form a cube, which one of the following (a, b, c, d, or e) is produced?

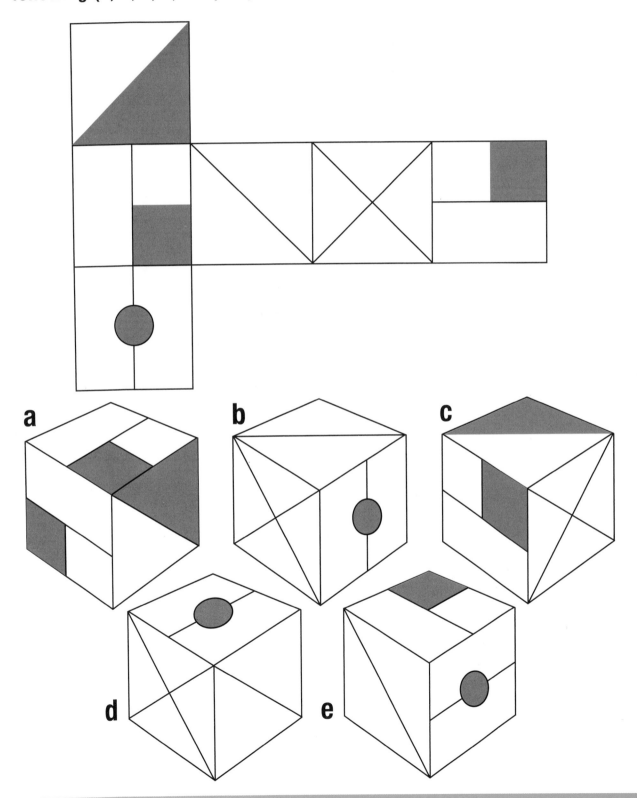

86 DIFFICULTY ✪✪✪✪✪✪✪☆☆
Target time: 7 minutes

Florence played a game of Snakes and Ladders with her brother Tom. He threw the first 6, so he started first, placing his playing piece on square 6. After that, every time it was Florence's turn, her die followed the sequence 6, 5, 4, 3, 2, 1; so her first move was to square 6, then to square 11, etc. After his first turn when he threw the 6, Tom's die followed the sequence 1, 2, 3, 4, 5, 6 each time, so his second move was to square 7, his third was to 9, etc. The normal rules of the game were followed, so whenever someone landed on a square that had the foot of a ladder, the piece was moved to the top of the ladder. Whenever someone landed on a square that had the head of a snake, the piece was moved to the tail of the snake. The number thrown to end the game didn't necessarily matter, since the first person to move a piece completely off the board won. Who won the game—Florence or Tom?

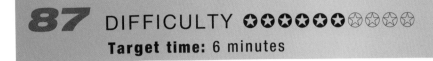

87 DIFFICULTY ✪✪✪✪✪✪☆☆☆☆
Target time: 6 minutes

What color should be in the central triangle?

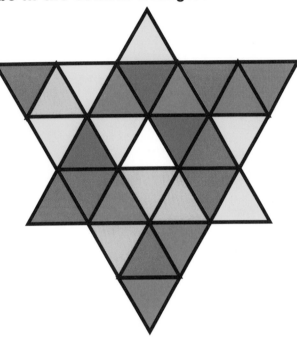

88 DIFFICULTY ✪✪✪✪✪✪✪☆☆☆
Target time: 7 minutes

It's impossible to color in this shape so that no two colors touch without using four different colors. What is the LEAST number of times in which you have to resort to using the fourth color (i.e., on how many areas)?

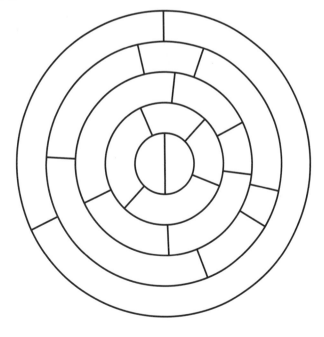

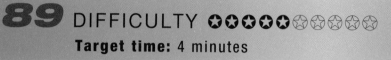

89 DIFFICULTY ★★★★☆☆☆☆☆
Target time: 4 minutes

In the puzzle below, which of the lettered squares (a, b, c, or d) fits into the empty space?

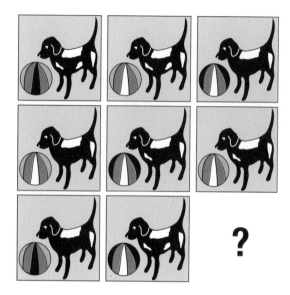

?

a   b

c   d

90 DIFFICULTY ★★★★☆☆☆☆☆
Target time: 4 minutes

Move one coin to make two rows of four in any direction.

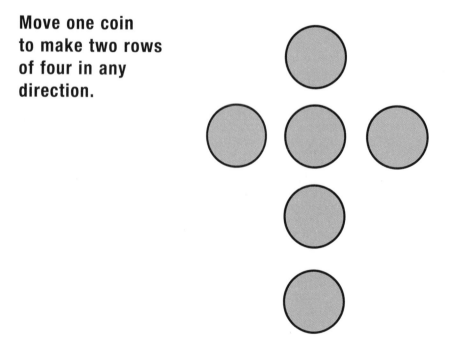

91 DIFFICULTY ✪✪✪✪✪✪✪✪✪
Target time: 10 minutes

Only two of these brick walls are identical. Can you determine which?

a

b

c

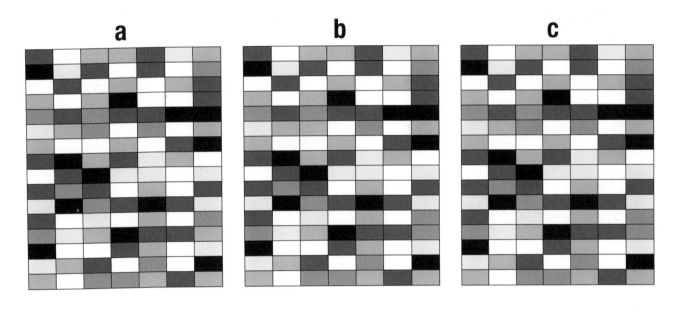

d

e

f

92 DIFFICULTY ✪✪✪✪✪✪☆☆☆☆
Target time: 6 minutes

Can you spot the eight differences between these two pictures? Circle them in the drawing on the right.

93 DIFFICULTY ✪✪✪✪✪✪✪✪✪☆
Target time: 7 minutes

Which three pieces of cut flower will fit together perfectly to form the flower seen on the right?

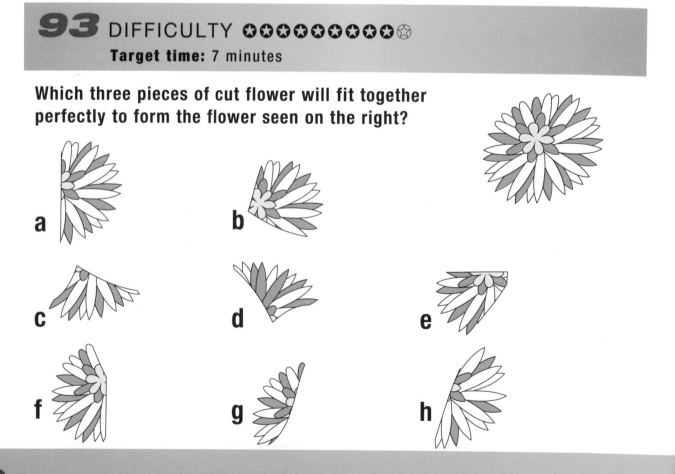

94 DIFFICULTY ✪✪✪✪☆☆☆☆☆☆
Target time: 5 minutes

Can you divide the clover leaf on the right by drawing two straight lines to produce four sections, each containing six different colors of flowers?

95 DIFFICULTY ✪✪✪✪✪☆☆☆☆☆
Target time: 3 minutes

If  is to

then is to:

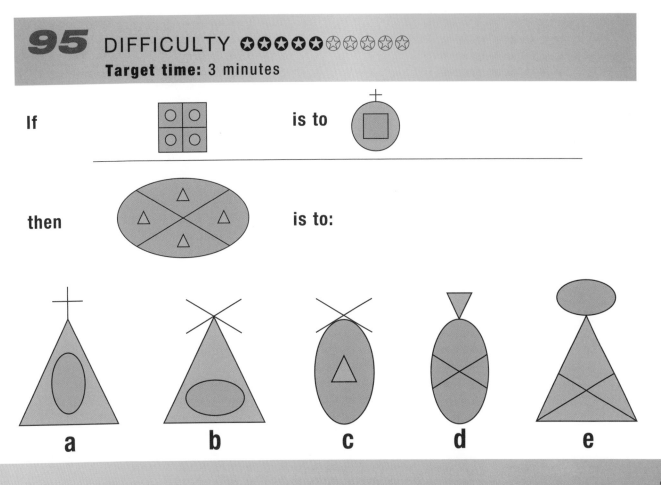

a   b   c   d   e

96 DIFFICULTY ✪✪✪✪✪✪✪☆☆☆
Target time: 7 minutes

Bob the Baker was asked to make six identical cakes, but one didn't turn out quite as planned—which is different from the others?

a

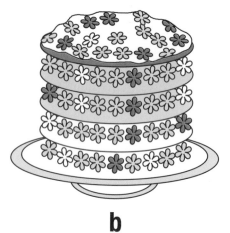

b

c

e

d

f

97 DIFFICULTY ✪✪✪✪✪✪✪✪✪✪

Target time: 6 minutes

Which of the four boxed figures (a, b, c, or d) completes the set?

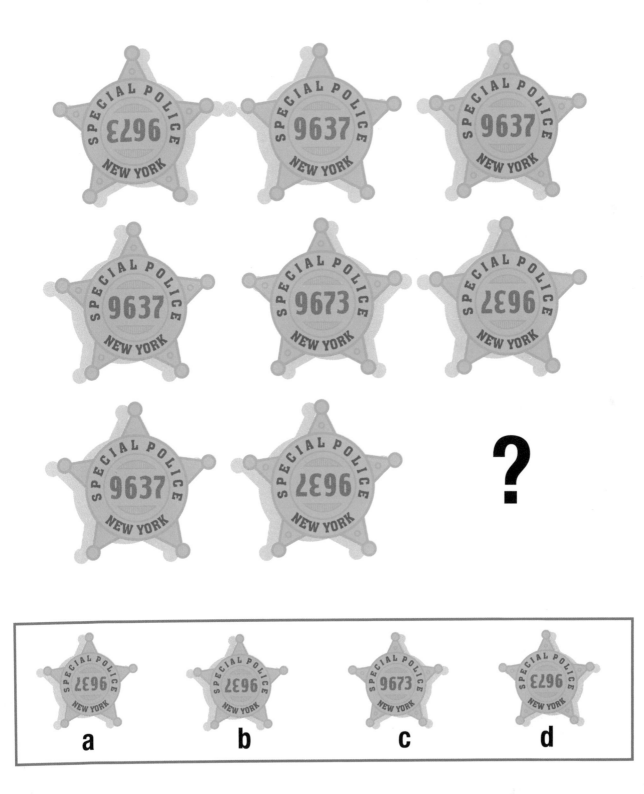

a   b   c   d

98 DIFFICULTY ⚬⚬⚬⚬⚬⚬☆☆☆☆
Target time: 5 minutes

Put three coins together so that they touch each other. Easy.

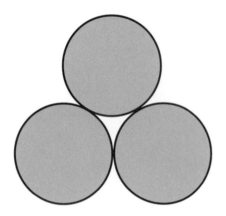

Now arrange four coins so they all touch. Not so difficult.

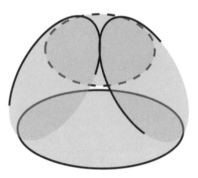

But can you arrange five so that they all touch?

99 DIFFICULTY ⚬⚬⚬⚬⚬⚬⚬☆☆☆
Target time: 6 minutes

What is the value of the missing domino?

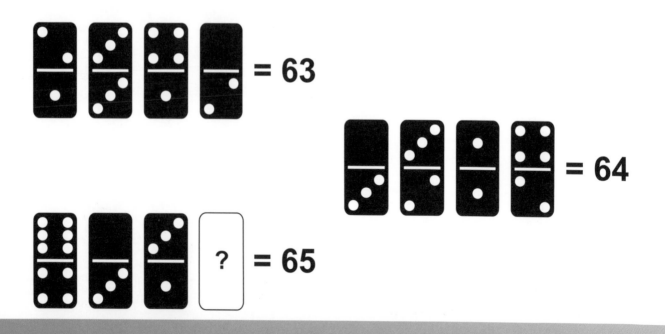

100 DIFFICULTY ✪✪✪✪✪✪✪✪✪✪✩
Target time: 7 minutes

Which four pieces of apple will fit together to form the apple below? Pieces may be rotated, but not flipped over.

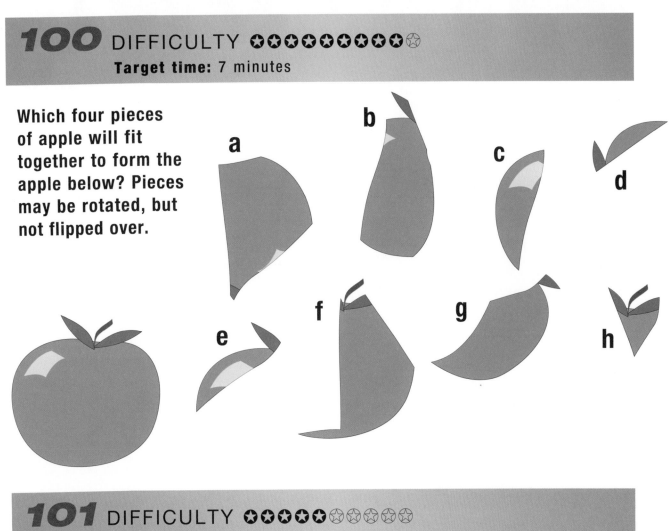

101 DIFFICULTY ✪✪✪✪✪✩✩✩✩✩
Target time: 4 minutes

In the sequence below, which of the lettered alternatives (a, b, c, or d) should replace the question mark?

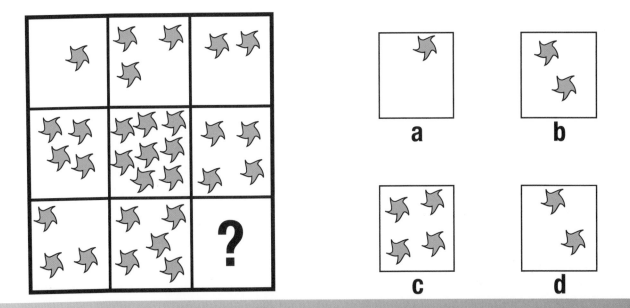

102 DIFFICULTY ✪✪✪✪✪☆☆☆☆

Target time: 6 minutes

Divide this sailing vessel by drawing three straight lines to produce four sections, each containing a ship's wheel, two anchors, and three ship's bells.

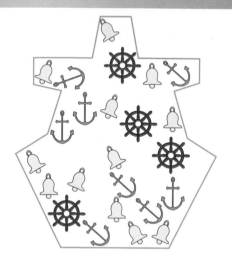

103 DIFFICULTY ✪✪✪✪✪✪✪☆☆

Target time: 5 minutes

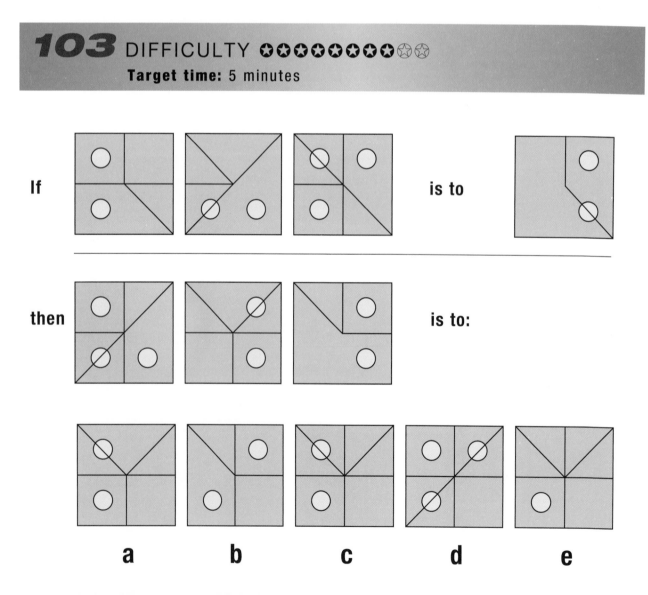

If ... is to ...

then ... is to:

a   b   c   d   e

Florence played a game of Snakes and Ladders with her brother Tom. He threw the first 6, so started first, placing his playing piece on the 6. After that, every time it was Florence's turn, her die followed the sequence 6, 5, 4, 3, 2, 1, so her first move was to square 6, then square 11, etc. After his first turn when he threw the 6, Tom's die followed the sequence 1, 2, 3, 4, 5, 6 each time, so his second move was to square 7, his third was to 9, etc. The normal rules of the game were followed, so whenever someone lands on a square that has the foot of a ladder, the piece is moved to the top of the ladder. Whenever someone lands on a square that has the head of a snake, the piece is moved to the tail of the snake. The number thrown to end the game didn't necessarily matter, since the first person to move a piece completely off the board wins. Who won the game: Florence or Tom—or neither? If one or both children cannot win, can you see why?

FINISH

100	99	98	97	96	95	94	93	92	91
81	82	83	84	85	86	87	88	89	90
80	79	78	77	76	75	74	73	72	71
61	62	63	64	65	66	67	68	69	70
60	59	58	57	56	55	54	53	52	51
41	42	43	44	45	46	47	48	49	50
40	39	38	37	36	35	34	33	32	31
21	22	23	24	25	26	27	28	29	30
20	19	18	17	16	15	14	13	12	11
1	2	3	4	5	6	7	8	9	10

START

105 DIFFICULTY ✪✪✪✪✪✪☆☆☆

Target time: 7 minutes

Only two of these tea canisters are exactly identical.
Can you determine which two?

a   b   c

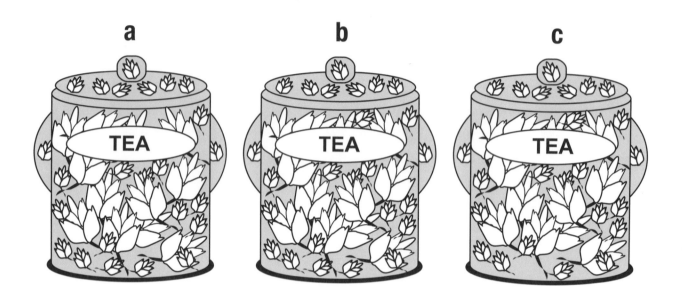

d   e   f

106 DIFFICULTY ✪✪✪✪✪✪✪✩✩

Target time: 5 minutes

In the sequence below, which of the lettered alternatives (a, b, c, or d) should replace the question mark?

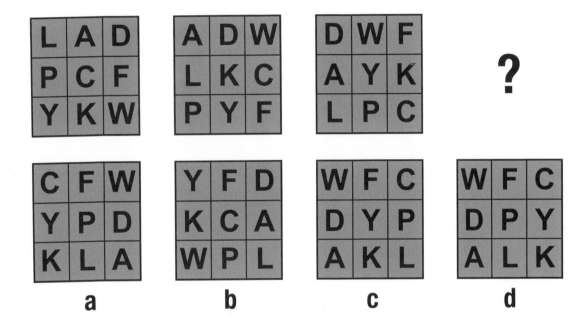

?

a   b   c   d

107 DIFFICULTY ✪✪✪✪✪✪✪✪✪✪

Target time: 10 minutes

Place the given dominoes into the spaces in the grid on the right in such a way that the number of dots in each of the four horizontal rows totals eighteen, and the number of dots in each of the six vertical columns totals twelve.

108 DIFFICULTY ✪✪✪✪✪✪✪✩✩
Target time: 8 minutes

Which shapes go in the highlighted rectangle to complete the hidden sequence?

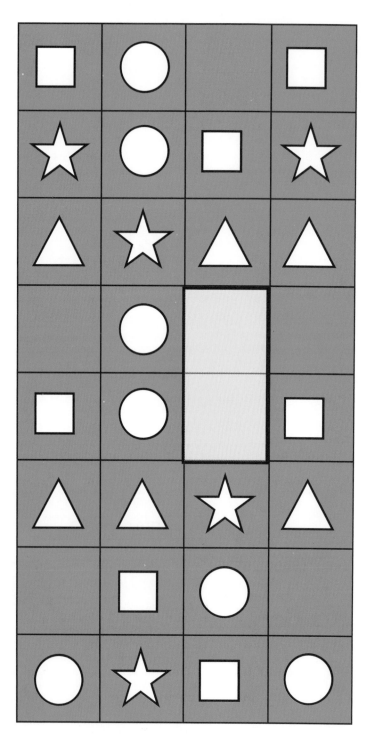

109 DIFFICULTY ✪✪✪✪✪✪✪✪✪
Target time: 10 minutes

Make your way from a to b through this honeycomb maze.

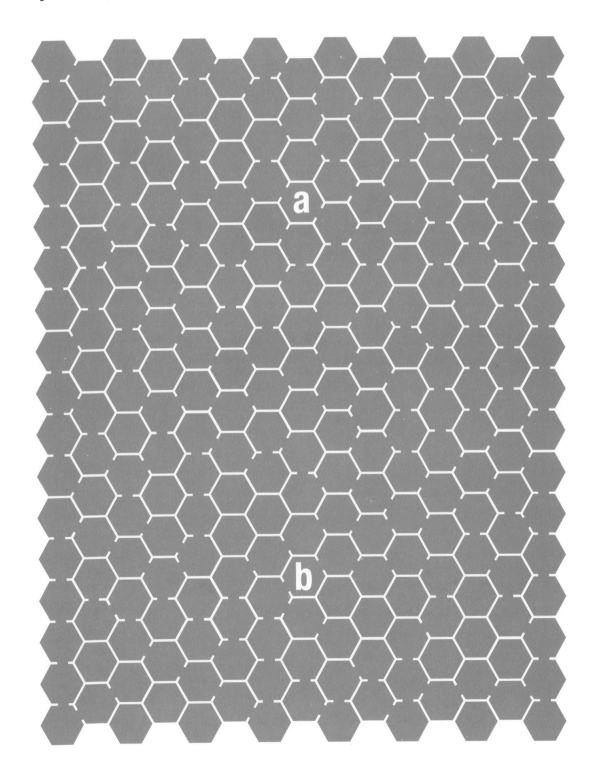

110 DIFFICULTY ★★★★★★★★★★

Target time: 10 minutes

Young Bill the builder has been busy. In each of the four buildings below, one brick is used more or less frequently than it is in the other three buildings. Can you determine the different brick in each construction? The ten brick types are as follows:

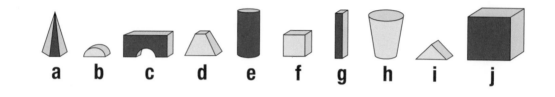

a   b   c   d   e   f   g   h   i   j

Building 1   **Building 2**

Building 3   **Building 4**

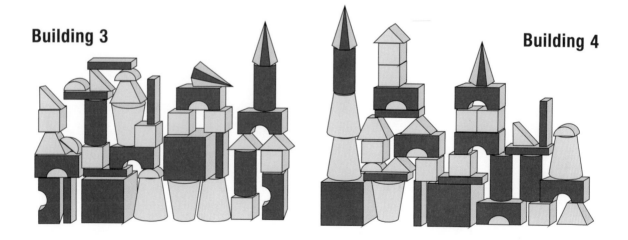

111 DIFFICULTY ✪✪✪✪✪✪✪☆☆☆
Target time: 20 minutes

Wait till you "sea" how this nonogram turns out! (See puzzle 6 for advice on how to complete a nonogram.)

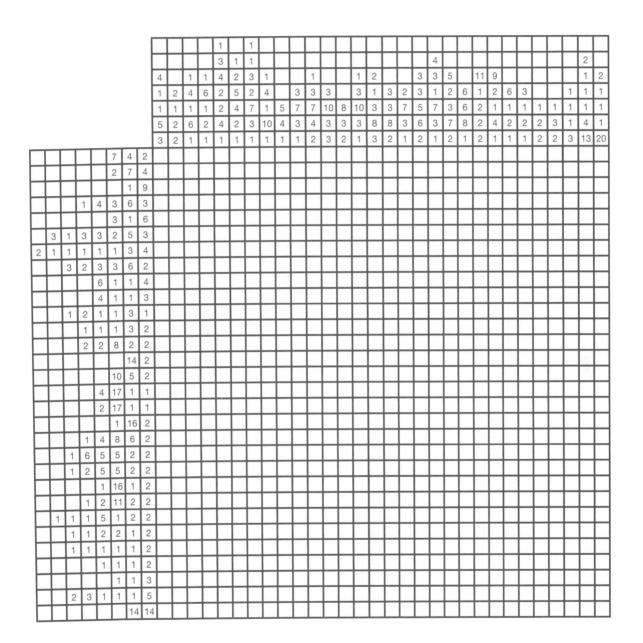

When the shape below is folded to form a cube, which one of the following (a, b, c, d, or e) is produced?

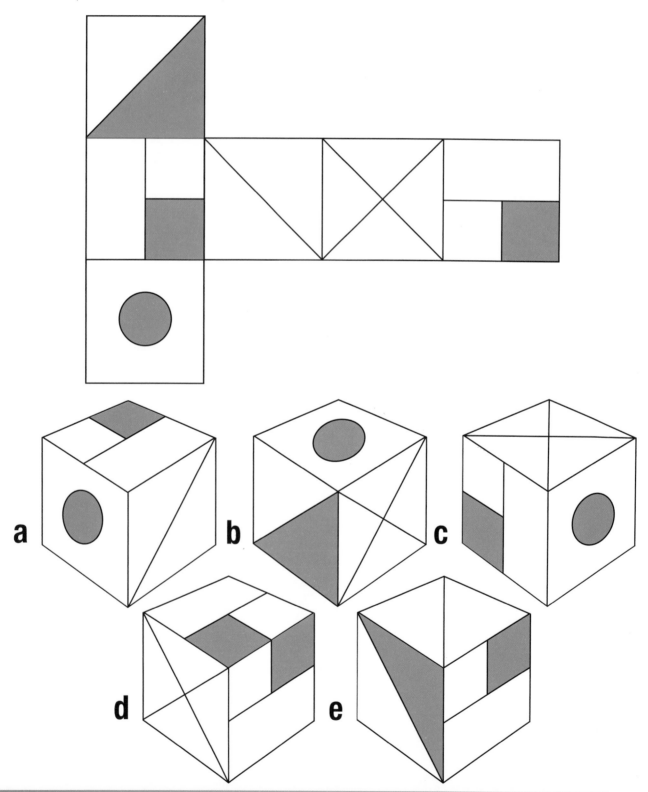

113 DIFFICULTY ✪✪✪✪✪☆☆☆☆☆
Target time: 5 minutes

Can you spot the ten differences between these two pictures?
Circle them in the drawing on the right.

114 DIFFICULTY ✪✪✪✪✪✪✪☆☆☆
Target time: 7 minutes

Connect all five pairs of like dots with continuous unbroken lines. All the lines run up, down, left, or right along the grid lines—none is a diagonal. No two lines should cross or touch, even at corners.

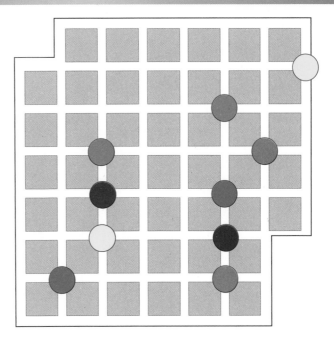

115 DIFFICULTY ✪✪✪✪✪✪✪☆☆
Target time: 7 minutes

Divide this picture by drawing four straight lines to produce five sections, each containing five different household items from a possible choice of seven.

116 DIFFICULTY ✪✪✪☆☆☆☆☆☆☆
Target time: 3 minutes

In the octagonal sequence shown on the right, which of the alternatives (a, b, c, d, or e) should replace the missing piece from this curious-looking pie?

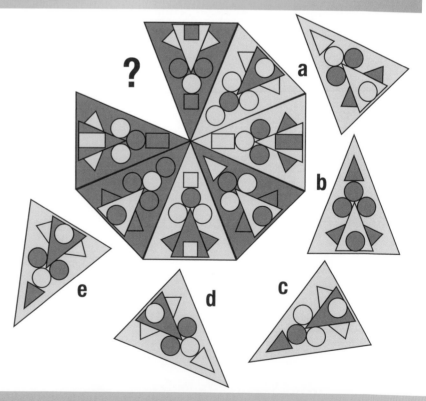

117 DIFFICULTY ✪✪✪✪✪✪✪☆☆☆

Target time: 7 minutes

Below are six identical jigsaw puzzles, each with a piece missing. Can you determine which of the numbered pieces is needed to complete each puzzle?

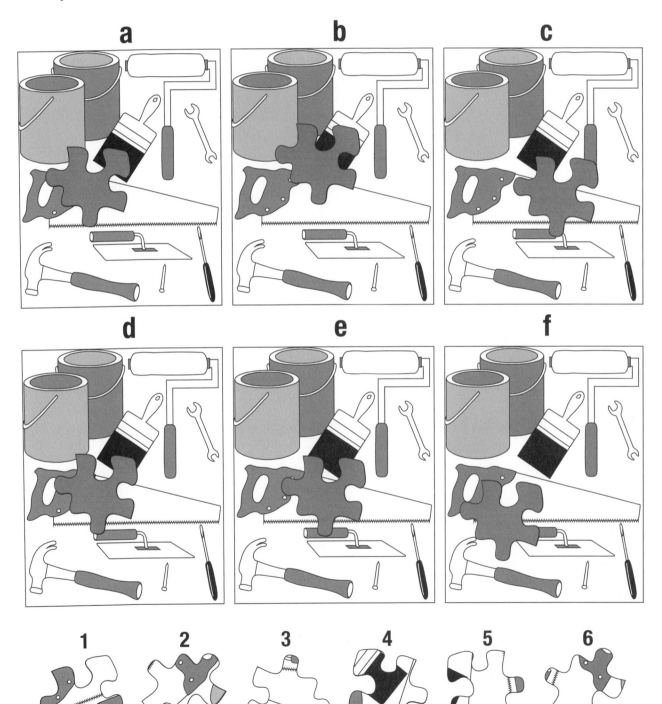

118 DIFFICULTY ⭐⭐⭐⭐⭐⭐☆☆☆
Target time: 5 minutes

Match the eight arrow flights with the correct arrowheads. If you pick the correct ones, an appropriate word will be spelled out.

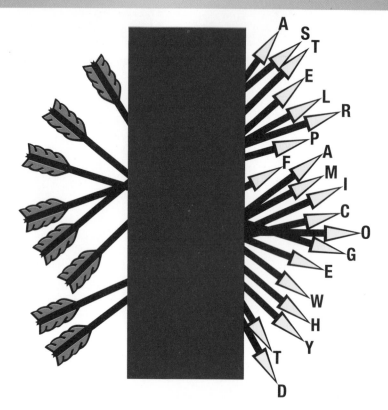

119 DIFFICULTY ⭐⭐⭐⭐⭐⭐⭐☆☆☆
Target time: 7 minutes

Can you spot the ten differences between these two pictures? Circle them in the drawing on the right.

120 DIFFICULTY ★★★★★☆☆☆☆☆
Target time: 3 minutes

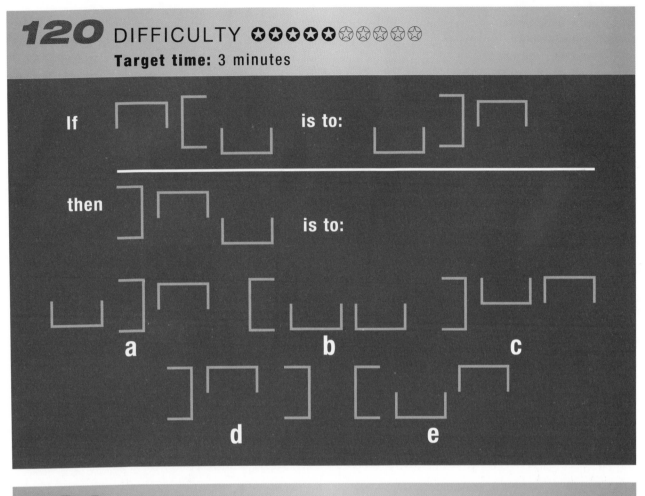

If [ ] is to: [ ]

then [ ] is to:

a   b   c

d   e

121 DIFFICULTY ★★★★★★★★☆☆
Target time: 5 minutes

In the puzzle below, which of the lettered squares (a, b, c, or d) fits into the empty space?

?

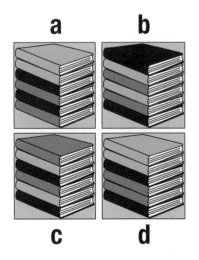

a   b

c   d

122 DIFFICULTY ✪✪✪✪✪✪☆☆☆☆
Target time: 6 minutes

You can't tell which way up these coins are just by touch, but you do know that half are heads and half are tails-side up. Can you, while blindfolded, divide them into two piles so that each pile has the same number of coins heads-side up?

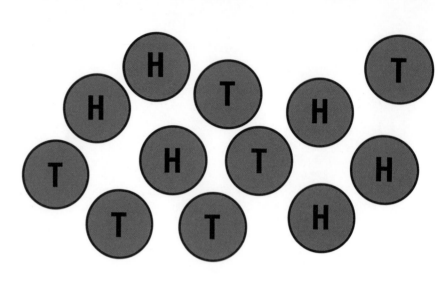

123 DIFFICULTY ✪✪✪✪✪✪✪✪✪✪
Target time: 10 minutes

The archaeologists at the museum of antiquities are having a hard time piecing together six pots they discovered at a recent dig. Can you match the correct missing piece with each vase to finish the task?

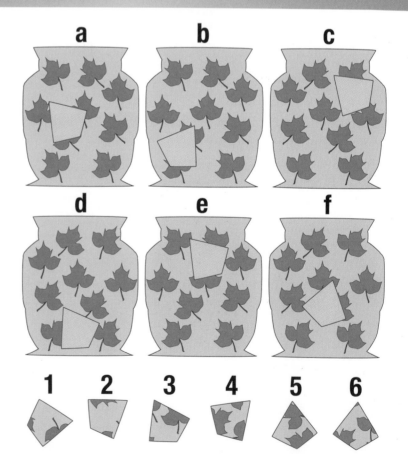

124 DIFFICULTY ✪✪✪✪✪✪✪☆☆☆
Target time: 7 minutes

Can you divide the picture on the right by drawing three straight lines to produce four sections, each containing different quantities (six, seven, eight, and ten) of assorted shapes? No section contains more than one of each shape.

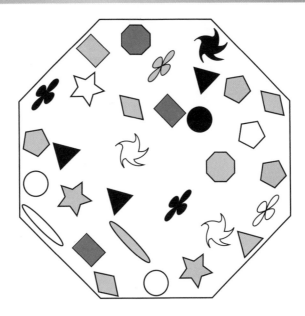

125 DIFFICULTY ✪✪✪✪✪✪✪✪☆☆
Target time: 6 minutes

Study this map of an island for one minute, then see if you can answer the questions on the next page without checking back.

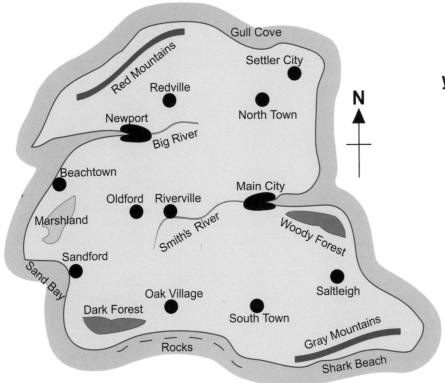

[125] DIFFICULTY ✪✪✪✪✪✪✪☆☆⭐

Target time: 6 minutes

Can you answer these questions about the puzzle on the previous page without checking back?

1. Which town lies directly west of North Town?

2. Which mountain range is furthest south?

3. On which river does Riverville stand?

4. What geographical feature is directly west of Oldford?

5. Which town or city is furthest north?

6. Which town or city is furthest east?

7. Which river runs through Newport?

8. Which is the nearest forest to Sand Bay?

126 DIFFICULTY ✪✪✪☆☆☆☆⭐☆⭐

Target time: 2 minutes

Which number should replace the question mark?

 = 11

= 50

= 24

 = ?

127 DIFFICULTY ✪✪✪✪✪✪✪✪✪✪

Target time: 10 minutes

Can you pair each of the stamps with its correct print?

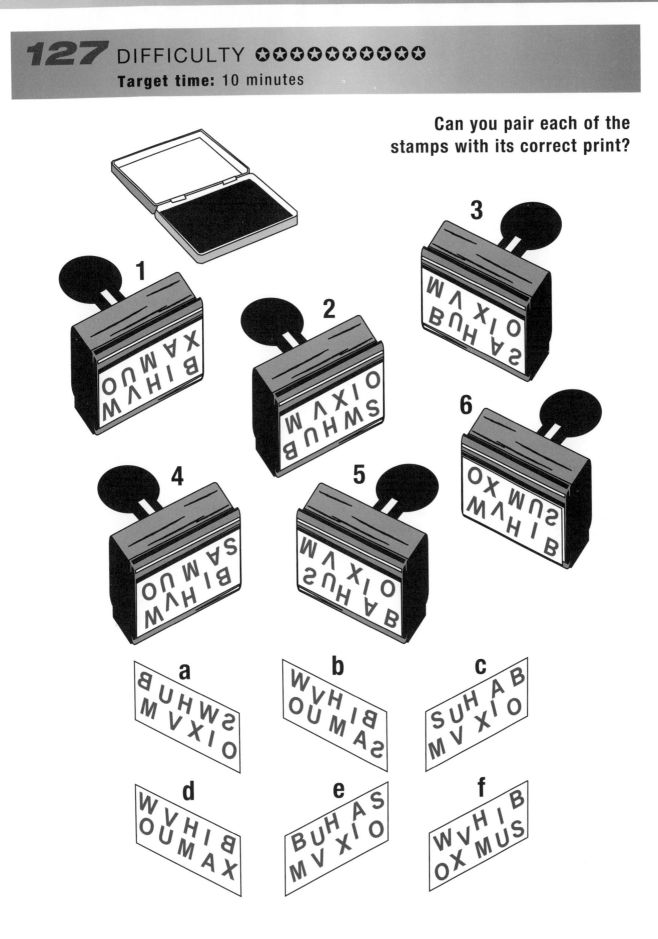

128 DIFFICULTY ✪✪✪✪✪✪☆☆☆☆
Target time: 6 minutes

Divide this picture by drawing four straight lines to produce six sections, each containing six different shapes in six different colors.

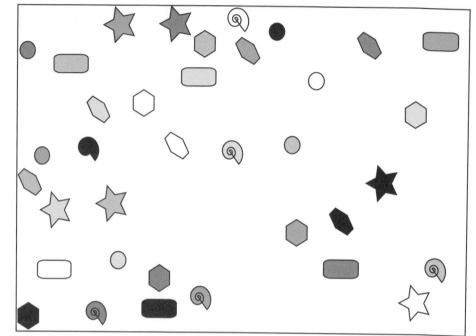

129 DIFFICULTY ✪✪✪✪✪✪✪☆☆☆
Target time: 7 minutes

Can you pair these door keys with the impressions of their ends? Take care though—first impressions may not be what they seem—some could be mirror images!

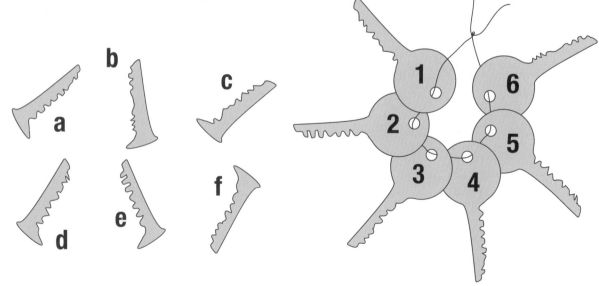

130 DIFFICULTY ✪✪✪✪✪✪✪✪☆

Target time: 7 minutes

This shape can be folded up to make a cube with a single continuous line around it. But there's been a mistake. Which face is wrong? Can you tell without making the cube? Can you also tell what should be on that face to make the line continuous?

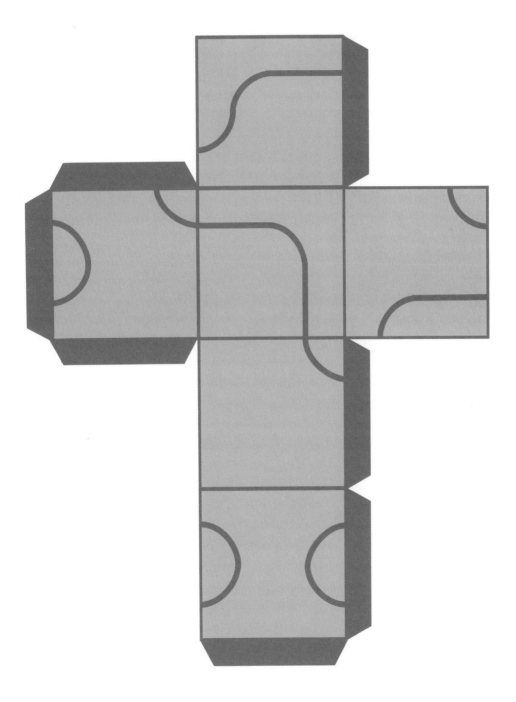

131 DIFFICULTY ✪✪✪✪✪✪✪✪✪✪
Target time: 7 minutes

In the sequence below, which of the lettered alternatives (a, b, c, or d) should replace the question mark?

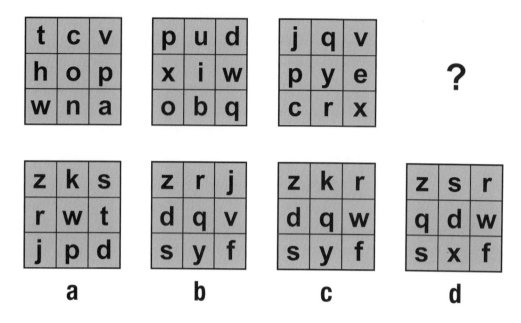

?

a   b   c   d

132 DIFFICULTY ✪✪✪✪✪✩✩✩✩✩
Target time: 4 minutes

In the sequence below, which of the lettered alternatives (a, b, c, or d) should replace the question mark?

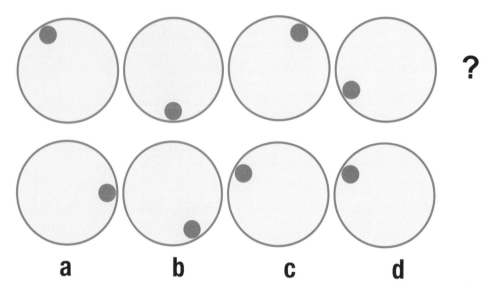

a   b   c   d

133 DIFFICULTY ✪✪✪✪✪✪✪✪✪✪

Target time: 10 minutes

Tom and Jim have been busy building walls. In each of the four walls below, one brick is used more or less frequently than it is in the other three walls. Can you determine the different brick in each construction? The ten brick types are as follows:

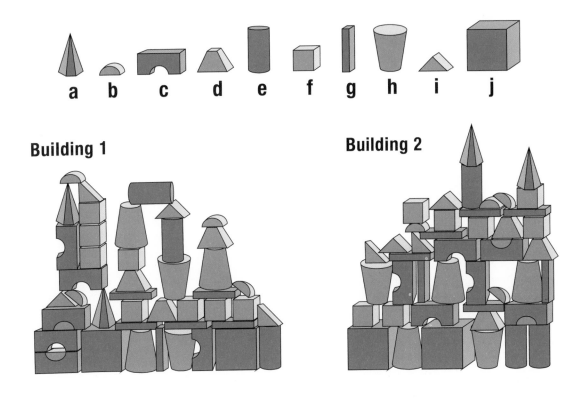

a b c d e f g h i j

Building 1

Building 2

Building 3

Building 4

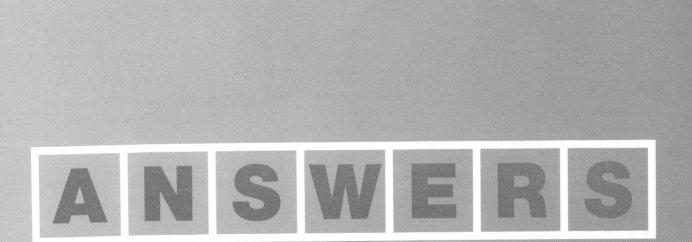

1

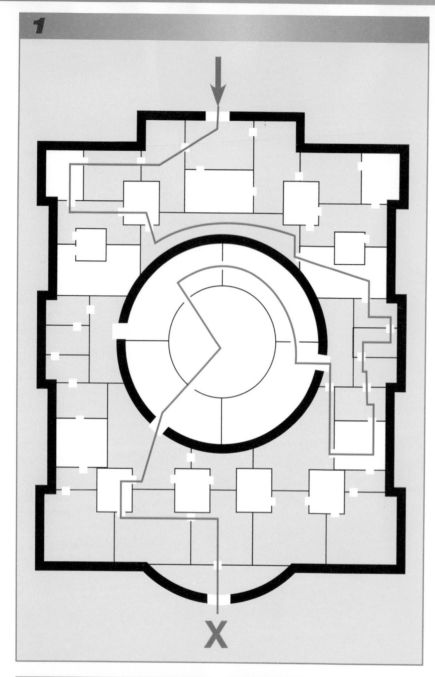

X

4

5

Twelve; the opposite sides of a die add up to seven, so the bottom three faces are (from left to right) two spots, four spots, and six spots, thus a total of twelve.

6

2

Whatever move your opponent performs, make the diametrically opposite move on your next turn. For example, if your opponent takes the coin in the top left corner, you take the coin in the bottom right corner.

3

1. 2
2. 1
3. 0
4. 0
5. 3
6. 2 + 1 = 3
7. 1 + 1 = 2
8. 12

7

8

d; each line contains two white stars and a yellow star, and each line also has a circled star. Each line contains a red and blue halved circle that has been turned through 0 degrees, 90 degrees, and 180 degrees (resulting in two lines running from top to bottom and one line from side to side). The missing image should contain a white star and a circle that has been turned through 90 degrees (i.e., runs from side to side).

9

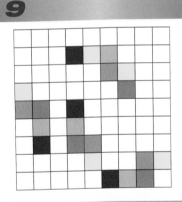

10

c   d

11

d

12

a; the top number of each is the sum of the previous top and bottom numbers, the bottom number is the difference between the top and bottom numbers on the previous domino, as well as being the difference between the total number of dots on both dominoes.

13

Twenty-three; Angelica can see the top faces of all three dice, thus a total of twelve spots. The opposite sides of a die add up to seven. On the furthest left die, the side face Angelica can see has two spots. On the central die, the side face Angelica can see has three spots. On the furthest right die, the side face Angelica can see has five spots. On the bottom face of the furthest right die, there are four spots, and the end face of this die (invisible to you) doesn't have six spots (intro), so must have one. Thus Angelica can see a total of twelve spots on the top faces, ten spots on the side faces and one on the end face, so a combined total of twenty-three spots.

14

One spot. ⊙
To determine why, look at each row, either going from side to side or on a diagonal from right to left or left to right. In each of these three possible directions, the row must contain all odd-numbered circles or all even-numbered circles. Going from right to left (or vice versa) the row in which the middle circle appears contains a five spot and a one spot, so it follows that the middle circle must contain another odd spot (in this case a one). Similarly, from bottom right to top left, the row contains a one, another odd number.

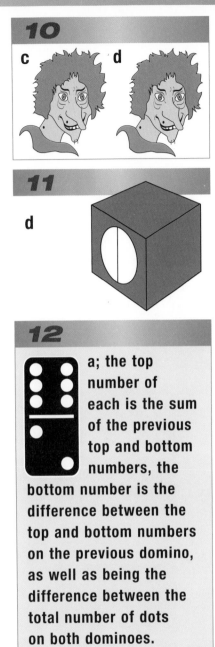

15

e; (it has more diamonds toward the nib of the pen).

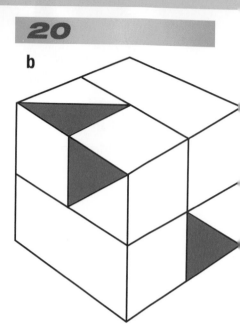

16

Two colors

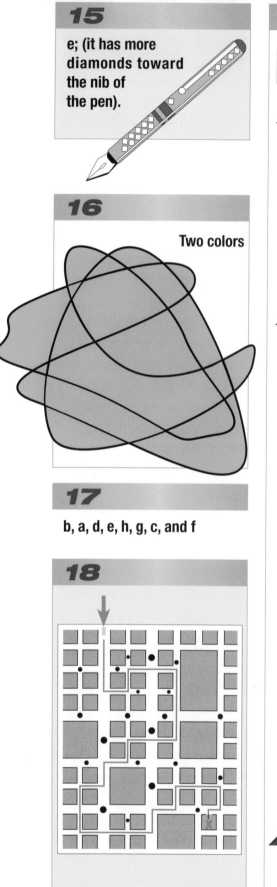

17

b, a, d, e, h, g, c, and f

18

19

a

b

c

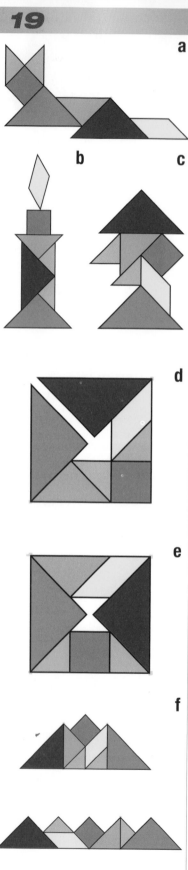

d

e

f

20

b

21

b; each line contains one dog with a white ear, two dogs with a patched eye, and two dogs with their tongues out. The missing image must have a white patched eye, no white ear, and its tongue hanging out.

22

a and c

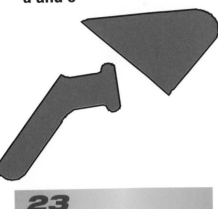

23

b; the total number of dots increases in number first by one, then by two, then by three, and finally by four, so the final number of dots must equal twelve.

24

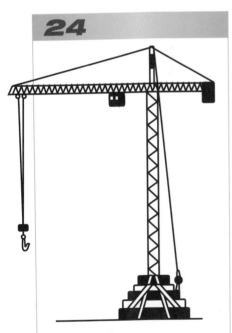

a; the struts at the base are closer together and do not extend to the outside edge of the base.

25

Each square contains a symbol with one side more or one side less than its immediate neighbor (above, below, left, right). Each symbol is also a color with one letter in its name more or one letter less than its immediate neighbor, e.g., red, blue, green, yellow, apricot.

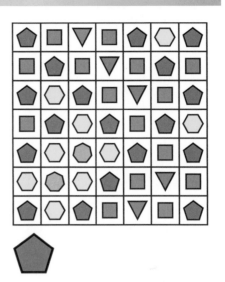

26

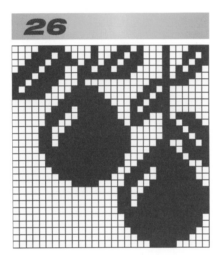

27

28

Four colors are needed.

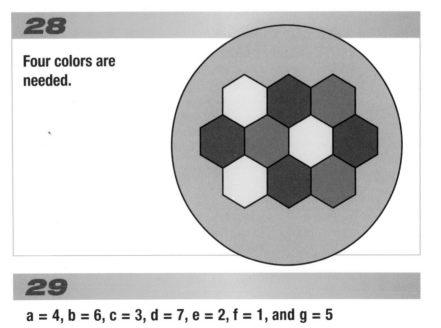

29

a = 4, b = 6, c = 3, d = 7, e = 2, f = 1, and g = 5

30

Domino 3/3 must be used with a 3 at the other corner and since there is only one other 3 (attached to a 1, totaling 4), the next corner is a 5. There is only one 5 (attached to a 2), so the corner is 2. Since the remaining corner of this side is a 3, this must be domino 2/4. Thus (similarly any rotation or reflection):

Domino 1/2 must be used with a 6 at the corner. This is attached to the 2, which requires a corner domino of 1, so 1/4. The corner of this side must be 4, part of domino 4/4, so this is next to corner 1, part of domino 1/2. Thus (similarly any rotation or reflection):

31

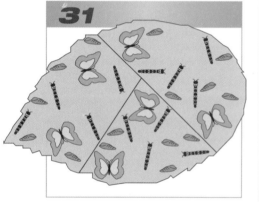

32

1. Pink
2. Red
3. 3
4. 3
5. 1
6. 2
7. 3
8. 4

34

c; each line contains two tic-tac-toe games where Xs win and one where Os win.
Each line contains a pink, an orange, and a blue square.
Each line contains two white games and a yellow game.
The winning game must therefore have an X win, a pink square, and a yellow game.

33

35

a

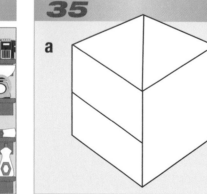

36

a and d

37

Start: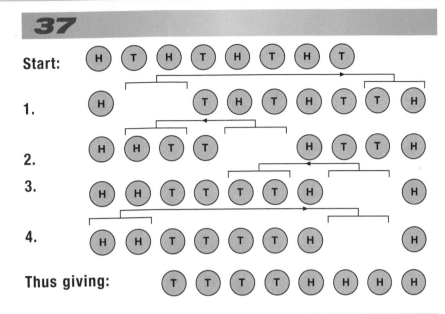

Thus giving:

38

The number in square 31 isn't 6 (clue 2), so in diagonal 6–31, square 21 = 6. Square 36 isn't 3 (clue 3), so in diagonal 1–36, square 15 = 3; and in 6–36, 24 = 3. Square 31 is 5 or 2 (2) as is 32 (1), so 36 is neither, thus 36 = 6 and 25 = 6 (3). Square 8 isn't 6 (diagonal), so in 2–32, square 2 = 6; thus 10 = 6. In 13–18, the 1 isn't in 14 (2), so must be in 13. Since there's a 5 in 22, there isn't a 5 in 1 or 19, so in 1–31, 31 = 5; so 14 = 5 (2), 32 = 2, and 3 = 2 (1). By elimination, 1 = 4, 8 = 1, 19 = 2, 20 = 4, 9 = 5, 27 = 1, 29 = 2 (diagonal), 11 = 4 (diagonal), 16 = 2, 28 = 4, 30 = 5, 4 = 3, 5 = 5, 12 = 2, 18 = 4, 23 = 1, 35 = 3, and 34 = 1.

4	6	2	3	5	1
3	1	5	6	4	2
1	5	3	2	6	4
2	4	6	5	1	3
6	3	1	4	2	5
5	2	4	1	3	6

39

11:35; the hour hand moves back by four hours (or forward by eight hours) and the minute hand moves forward by seven minutes each time.

40

b

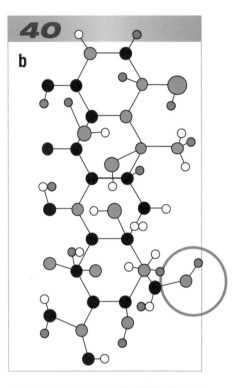

41

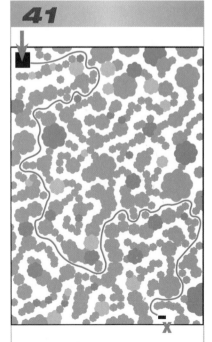

42

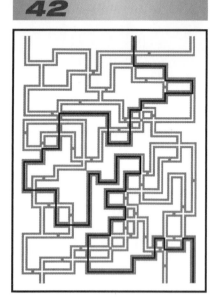

43

It is possible to do with three colors.

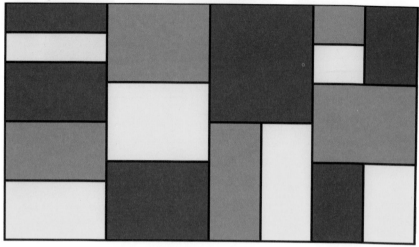

44

1	5	4	6	3	2
2	3	6	5	1	4
6	1	2	3	4	5
3	2	5	4	6	1
4	6	1	2	5	3
5	4	3	1	2	6

The number in row four, column four cannot be 1 or 2 (horizontal) or 3 or 5 (diagonal) or 6 (vertical), so it must be 4. Similarly, row six, column six cannot be 1, 2, 3, 4, or 5, so it must be 6. To complete the diagonal column one, row one must be 1. In row four, the 5 cannot be in column one or five, so it must be column three. The total of the four corner spots is 14 (intro) so row one, column six is 2. The top right to bottom left diagonal contains five different numbers and no 4, so row three, column four is not 2, 4, 5, or 6 so it must be 1 or 3. As neither row five, column two nor row two, column five can be a 3, row three, column four must be 3. Column six, row three must be 5, and row five 3. In row one, the 5 cannot be in column three or five, so it must be in column two. In column five, the 2 cannot be in rows one, three, or four so it must be in row six. In row six, the 3 cannot be in columns two or four so must be in column three, the 4 cannot be in column four so must be in column two, which leaves 1 in column four. The 5 in column four cannot be in row five, so it must be in row two, and the 2 in row five. In row two, the 2 cannot be in column three or five so it must be in column one. In column one, the 3 cannot be in rows three or five, so it must be in row four. Thus row four, column five is 6. In row one, the 3 is not in column three, so it must be in column five, and the 4 in column three. In row two the 6 is not in column five so it must be in column three, and the 1 in column five. Column five is thus completed by a 4 in row three. In row three, the 1 is not in column one, so it must be in column two, and the 6 in column one. Thus column one is completed by a 4, column two by a 6, and column three by a 1.

45

1

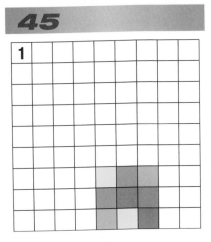

2

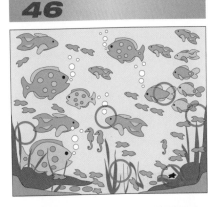

46

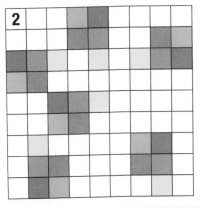

47

48

b and e

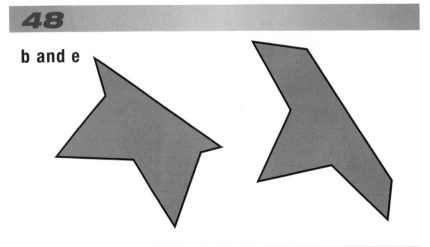

49

Two dominoes each total 9 (5/4 and 6/3). For these sides to total 10, both 1s must be corner numbers. Two dominoes each total 7 (5/2 and 4/3). They must each have 3 as a corner number, thus 3/4 and 3/6 (as 3/1 has a corner of 1, as described above). So one square has domino 3/4 with the 3 as a corner and the 3 of 3/6 as its other corner to total 10. Domino 3/6 must have 1 at its corner. If the 1 domino is 1/3, the corner is 6, thus 6/2 (6/3 has been used) but the final side would then total 11, which is incorrect. So the domino is 1/4, with 5 at the corner, hence 5/2 to make the correct total (see image below left).

The remaining dominoes form a square with domino 5/4 and a corner of 1, part of domino 1/3. To total 10, 1/3 has a corner of 6 from domino 6/2. which in turn has a corner of 2 from domino 2/4 (see image above right).

50

The bottom one. This results in the domino squares alternating between odd and even in rows and columns (except the fifth row, which is now incomplete).

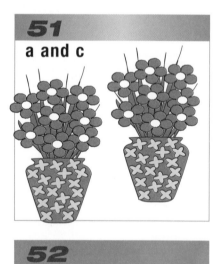

51

a and c

52

The shortest route is thirty moves, as follows: 2 to x, 6 to 2, 5 to a, x to 5, a to 6, 2 to c, 1 to x, c to 1, 6 to 2, 7 to a, 8 to b, 5 to 8, b to 5, x to 7, a to 6, 2 to c, 3 to x, 4 to b, 1 to 4, b to 1, c to 3, 6 to 2, 5 to a, x to 5, a to 6, 2 to c, 1 to x, c to 1, 6 to 2, x to 6.

53

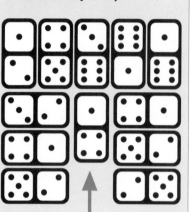

54

a; the large star rotates by a quarter turn counterclockwise, and the smaller shapes within it by a quarter turn clockwise every time.

55

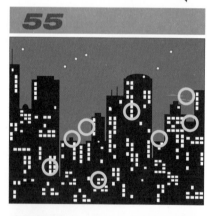

56

c; the total number of dots increases in number by two every time.

57

c and d

58

a and g are the same.

59

1d; each line contains two airships with red fins and one with blue fins. Each line contains two airships with red gondolas underneath and one with a blue gondola. Each line contains two airships facing left and one facing right. Each line contains two airships with four lights on the balloon and one with three lights. The missing image therefore has blue fins, a red gondola, faces left, and has four lights on the balloon, so it must be d.

60

Push the middle row up by moving the top coin to the bottom and using it to push up the whole column.

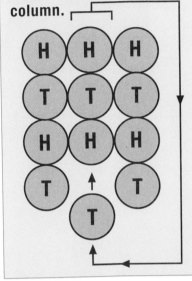

63

d; each shape becomes its reflection.

64

61

62

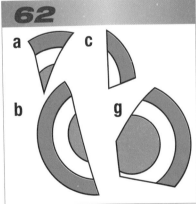

65

1. Orange
2. Orange
3. 2
4. 3
5. 3
6. 2
7. 3
8. Orange

66

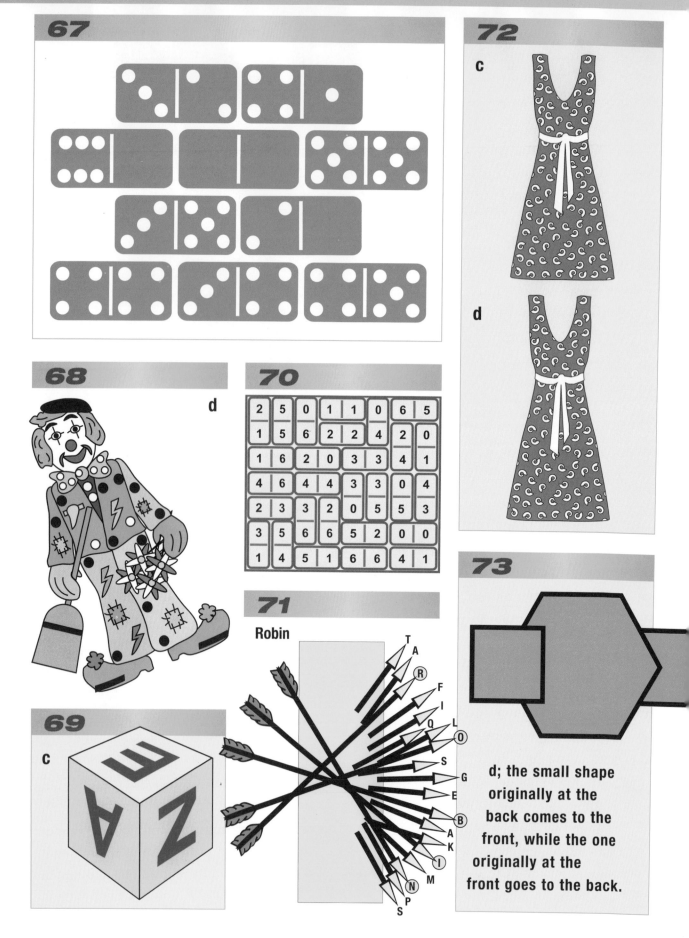

67

68

69
c

70

2	5	0	1	1	0	6	5
1	5	6	2	2	4	2	0
1	6	2	0	3	3	4	1
4	6	4	4	3	3	0	4
2	3	3	2	0	5	5	3
3	5	6	6	5	2	0	0
1	4	5	1	6	6	4	1

71

Robin

T
A
Ⓡ
F
I
Q
L
Ⓞ
S
G
E
Ⓑ
A
K
Ⓘ
M
N
P
S

72
c

d

73

d; the small shape
originally at the
back comes to the
front, while the one
originally at the
front goes to the back.

74

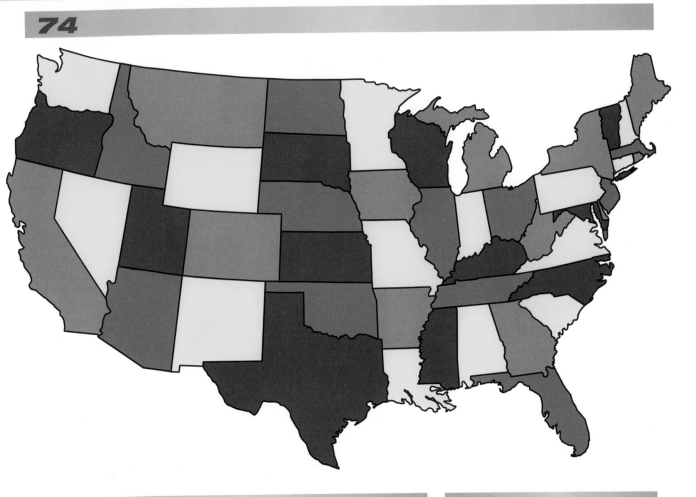

75

a; each line contains two signs that are right-side up, and one that is upside-down. Each line contains two "STOP"s with an exclamation point and one without. Each line contains one red "FILTERED" and two black. On each line the steam is colored white twice and yellow once. The missing image should be right-side up. "STOP" should have an exclamation point. "FILTERED" should be in black. The steam on the cup should be yellow, so it must be a.

76

77

Since the opposite two sides of a die have spots totaling seven, Peter gave double the quantity of the number of spots that appear on the opposite side of the die. The yellow die relates to the quantity of loaves, and the blue to the quantity of fish. Thus Mary was awarded four loaves and ten fish.

78

79

1. Barry
2. Roger
3. Tom
4. White
5. 5
6. 4

7. 3
   (Katie, Jane, and Anna)
8. 3
   (Will, Mary, and Jane)

80

1. e and f
2. g
3. 3
4. 1
5. 1

6. 8
7. 1
8. 30

81

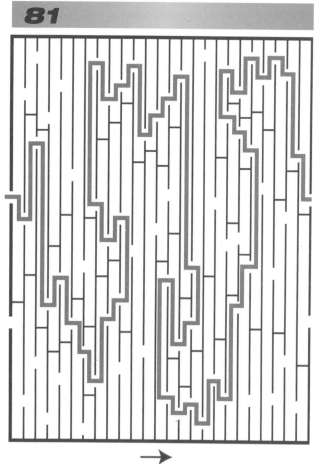

82

Pattern a can be found six times.

a   b

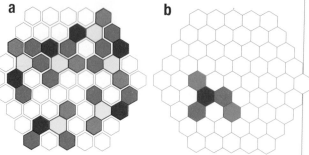

83

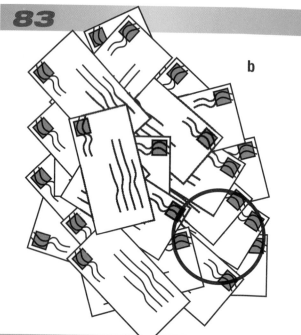

b

84

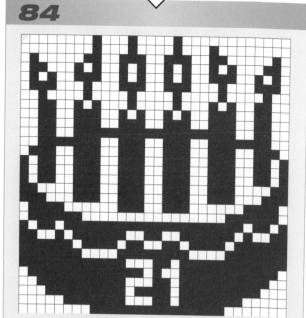

85

d

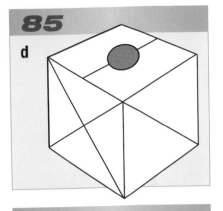

86

Tom

87

Green. Each set of four triangles has 3 colors.

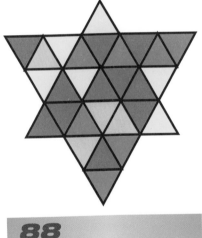

88

You need to resort to using it only once.

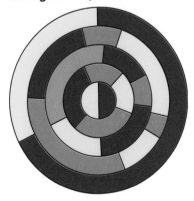

89

b; each different dog and each different ball appears three times. Thus the missing dog has three white spots and a ball with two green stripes, two red stripes, and one black stripe.

90

One answer is to place the topmost coin on top of the one at the center of the cross.

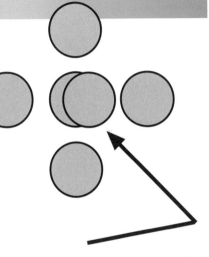

91

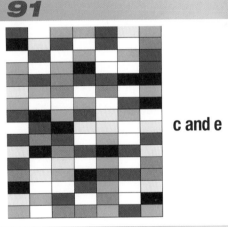

c and e

92

93

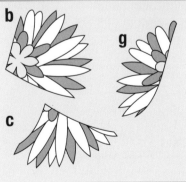

b

g

c

94

95

b; the four small triangles merge into one triangle that increases in size. The cross originally in the ellipse goes on top of the triangle. The ellipse reduces in size and goes inside the triangle.

96

f

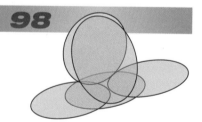

97

c; each line contains two badges with the number 9637 and one with the number 9673.
Each line contains two badges with the number right-side up and one with it upside-down.
Each line contains one badge with the circles on the points of the star removed. Each line contains two badges where the shadow falls to the left and one where it falls to the right.

The missing image should have the number 9673 and be right-side up. The circles on the points of the star should be intact and the shadow should fall to the right, so it must be c.

98

Place two coins on top of one coin, then balance another two coins so that they support each other and touch the three coins lying flat.

99

The missing domino is 0/1; the figure is derived by adding the total dots on the first two dominoes and multiplying the answer by the total dots on the second two dominoes.

100

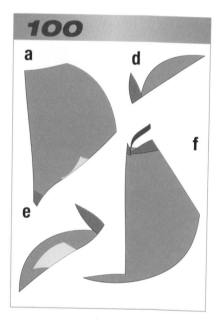

101

b; reading across any row or down any column, the sum of the outer two squares is equal to that of the inner square, so the missing square must have two shapes.

102

105

b and d

103

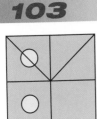

c; only lines that appear in the same position just twice in the first three squares are carried forward to the final square. Only circles that appear just once are carried forward.

106

d; each letter moves one place along in the direction of the arrow, as shown.

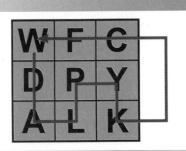

104

Tom can win, but Florence can't. Eventually, Florence reaches a point where she throws a 5 and lands on square 64. From there, her moves are: 68–87, 90, 92–72, 73, 79, 84–64, 68–87, 90, 92–72, 73, 79, 84–64, 68–87, 90, 92–72, etc.; thus her moves never get beyond square 92.

107

In the middle column of complete dominoes, the left-hand side of the missing dominoes must both be 0, and the right-hand sides are 1 + 3. In the third

horizontal row from the top, the central right-hand side of the middle domino can't be 1, so this domino is 0/3, thus 0/1 is the middle domino in the second row. The domino furthest right in the second horizontal row from the top is 5/5, thus the domino furthest left in the third row from the top is 6/6. The left-hand vertical column of complete dominoes has 0/0 and 0/5, so 0/0 is in the bottom row, and 0/5 in the top row. Domino 2/2 is in the top row, and the domino in the bottom row furthest right position is 3/4.

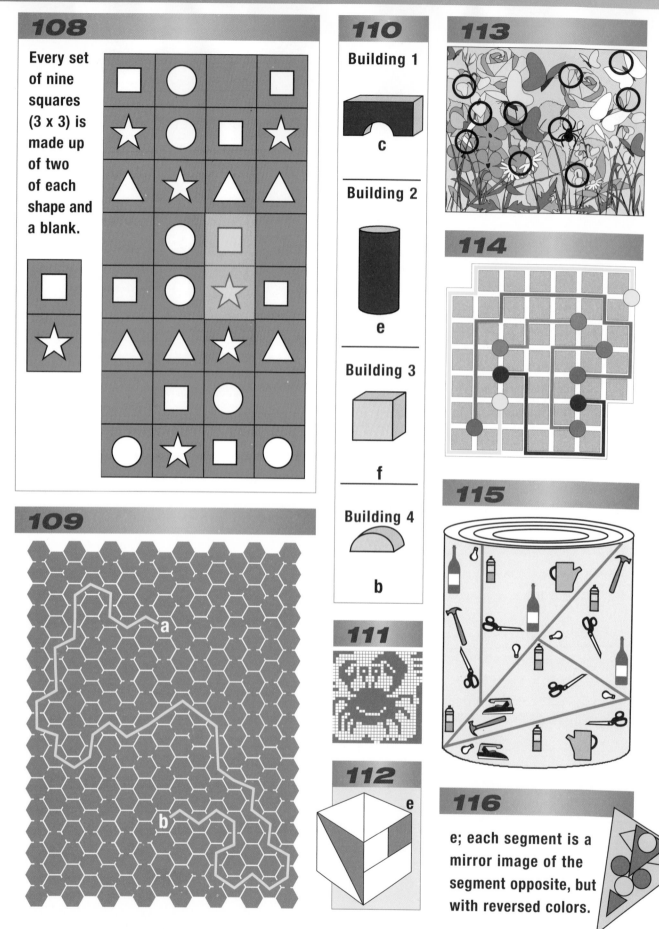

108

Every set of nine squares (3 x 3) is made up of two of each shape and a blank.

109

110

Building 1

c

Building 2

e

Building 3

f

Building 4

b

111

112

e

113

114

115

116

e; each segment is a mirror image of the segment opposite, but with reversed colors.

117

a = 2, b = 4, c = 3,
d = 6, e = 5, f = 1

118

Straight

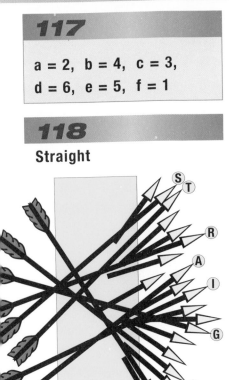

119

120

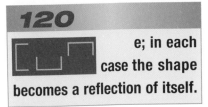

e; in each case the shape becomes a reflection of itself.

121

d; from left to right in each horizontal row, the lowest book moves to the top of the pile; and from top to bottom, in each vertical column, the two lowest books move to the top of the pile.

122

Divide the coins into two piles without turning any over. Then turn over every coin in one of the piles. Try it and see!

123

a = 4, b = 5, c = 1, d = 2, e = 6, f = 3

124

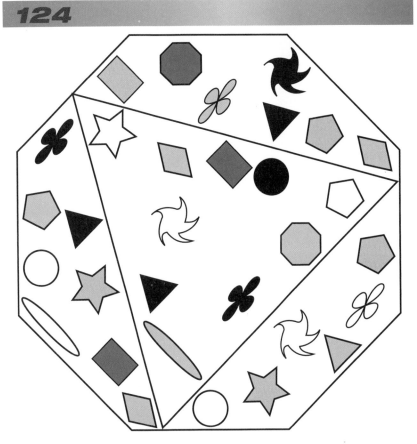

125

1. Redville
2. Gray Mountains
3. Smith's River
4. Marshland
5. Settler City
6. Saltleigh
7. Big River
8. Dark Forest

126

63; multiply the total number of dots on the first domino by the total number of dots on the second.

127

1 = d, 2 = a, 3 = e, 4 = b, 5 = c, 6 = f

128

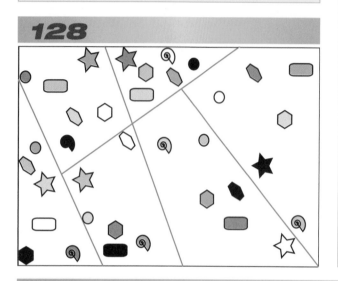

129

1 = c, 2 = e, 3 = f, 4 = a, 5 = d, 6 = b

130

When the original cutout shape is made into a cube there are two continuous lines. To have only one, there should be two horizontal lines on the face on the bottom of the diagram instead of two semicircles.

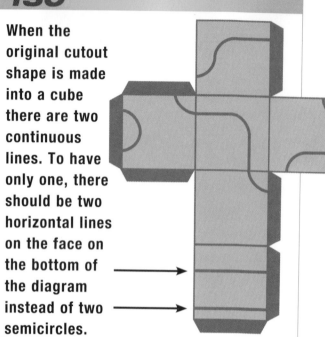

131

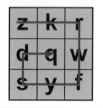

c; each letter moves one place on in the alphabet, then the central letter moves to the top left-hand corner, while the others move one place forward in the direction of the arrow, as shown.

132

a; think of this as being like a clock where the circle represents an hour number on the face—the hour moves back five places every time, so ends up at "3 o'clock," which is a.

133

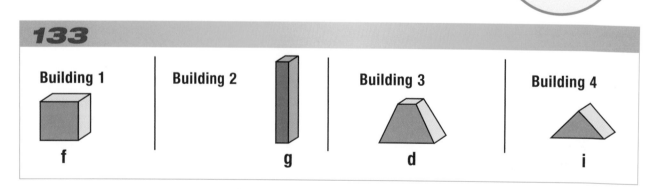

Building 1	Building 2	Building 3	Building 4
f	g	d	i

ACKNOWLEDGMENTS ✪ PERCEPTUAL PUZZLES

✪ Puzzle contributors

Contributors are listed next to the numbers of the puzzles they created.

✪ Brainwarp

Puzzles 14, 25, 37, 50, 60, 87, 90, 98, 108, 122, 130

✪ David Bodycombe

Puzzles 2, 9, 16, 19, 28, 43, 45, 52, 71, 74, 82, 88, 114, 118

✪ Guy Campbell

Puzzles 1, 7, 8, 18, 21, 34, 41, 42, 59, 64, 75, 81, 97, 109

✪ Philip Carter & Ken Russell

Puzzles 11, 20, 35, 63, 69, 85, 95, 103, 112, 120

✪ Puzzlemakers

Puzzles 3, 4, 5, 6, 10, 12, 13, 15, 17, 22, 23, 24, 26, 27, 29, 30, 31, 32, 33, 36, 38, 39, 40, 44, 46, 47, 48, 49, 51, 53, 54, 55, 56, 57, 58, 61, 62, 65, 66, 67, 68, 70, 72, 73, 76, 77, 78, 79, 80, 83, 84, 86, 89, 91, 92, 93, 94, 96, 99, 100, 101, 102, 104, 105, 106, 107, 110, 111, 113, 115, 116, 117, 119, 121, 123, 124, 125, 126, 127, 128, 129, 131, 132, 133

Perceptual Puzzles was commissioned, edited, designed, and produced by:
Librios Publishing Ltd., 21 Catherine Street, London WC2B 5JS, United Kingdom
Managing Director: Hal Robinson
Editor: Alison Moore **Project Editor:** Marilyn Inglis **Art Editor:** Keith Miller
Designers: Michael Chapman, Austin Taylor; Evelyn Bercott **Copy Editor:** Sarah Barlow

Spatial Puzzles

In this section of *Spatial Puzzles* we'll be improving your perception skills in both two and three dimensions and hopefully having fun along the way.

The ability to perceive things in three dimensions is becoming more important in our everyday lives. Computer programs are now able to take a two-dimensional image, such as a photograph, and apply it to a three-dimensional model so that a full-perspective image of a human face can be rendered. This technology can be used to help catch criminals or to see your face on the main character in a computer game! 3-D-style images such as holograms now play an important part in security and forgery protection.

One type of spatial skill is called "perceptual constancy." This means that, even though we see a car close to us in the street, we would know how that object would behave if we saw it again in the distance or on television. This also explains why our senses can become easily confused. When we go into a hall of mirrors at the fair or look at an optical illusion, our previous experience works against us and provides confusing yet amusing results. It is also the basis of some visual comedy and fun vacation photo snaps, where objects can appear out of scale.

Perceptions also have their place in aiding our experience of art. For instance, in Bridget Riley's artwork in the op art movement, where flat paintings give the impression of a 3-D surface. There are also of course the classic engravings and woodcuts of the Dutch graphic artist M. C. Escher (1898–1972), with his impossible-looking staircases.

So, before you dive headlong into this section, here's a few words of advice. All the puzzles have a time limit as a guide, but if you'd prefer to proceed at your own pace . . . who's to know?! You can just open a random page and find a puzzle that looks interesting. However, as that doesn't narrow it down much, be sure to pay attention to our special star grading system. Easier puzzles have one, two, or three stars. Eight, nine, or (ouch) ten stars means you're in danger of going boggle-eyed. You have been warned.

Every question is numbered and has its answer clearly marked in the back of the section. But be sure to try all avenues before resorting to the solutions—things are not always what they seem at first!

Our perception is that you're going to get a lot of enjoyment out of the puzzles within, so we won't delay you a moment more. Have fun! ✪

—David Bodycombe

1 DIFFICULTY ✪✪✪✪✪✩✩✩✩✩  ③ Minutes

Travel from one star's center to the other's center without crossing any lines.

2 DIFFICULTY ✪✪✪✪✪✪✪✪☆☆   ⏱ **5** Minutes

Using only straight lines, can you divide this rectangle into eight sections, each of identical shape and size, and each with four red circles?

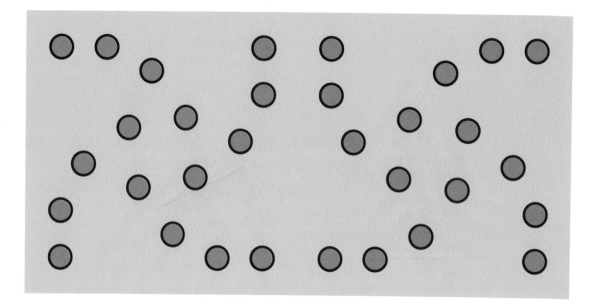

3 DIFFICULTY ✪✪✪✪☆☆☆☆☆☆   ⏱ **2** Minutes

Here are four matches. Can you move one match to leave two?

4 DIFFICULTY ✪✪✪✪☆☆☆☆☆☆   **4** Minutes

Can you pair this stamp with its correct print?

a

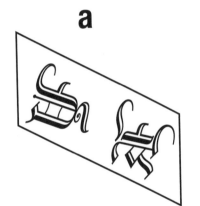

b

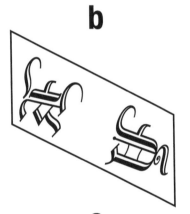

c

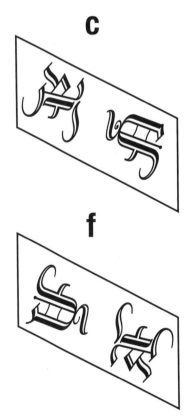

d

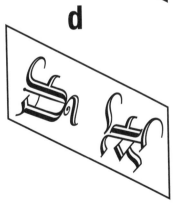

e

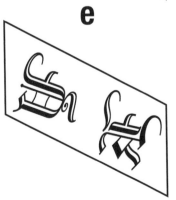

f

Which of the four boxed figures (a, b, c, or d) completes the set?

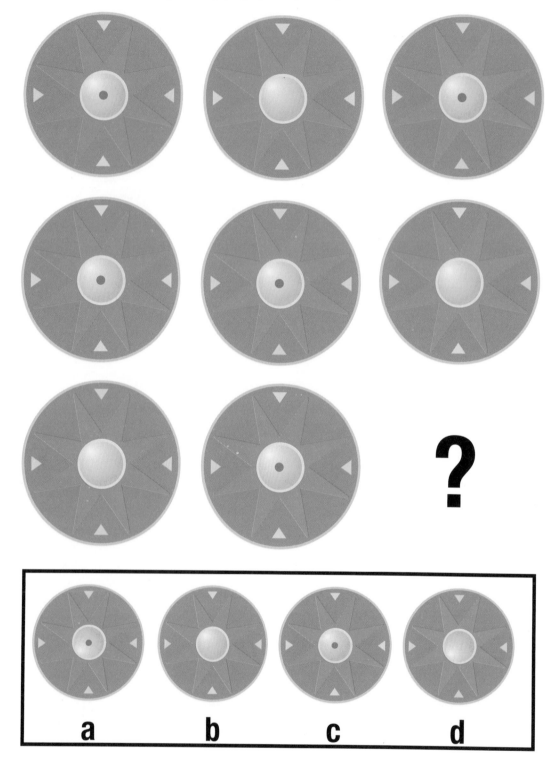

6 DIFFICULTY ✪✪✪✪✪☆☆☆☆☆   **6** Minutes

A famous mathematical theorem says that any political map (where no two bordering countries are colored the same) can be completed using just four colors. Grab four different pens and see if you can color the mainland of Europe correctly. Don't worry about the small islands.

7 DIFFICULTY ✪✪✪✪☆☆☆☆☆☆   **3** Minutes

Can you cut this cake into four slices, each containing the same number and type of decorations, with just two straight cuts of the knife? Although the knife may pass between the candles, no decoration may be cut!

8 DIFFICULTY ★★★★★☆☆☆★☆   **8** Minutes

Kirsty played a game of Snakes and Ladders with her brother Tom. He threw the first 6, so started first, placing his playing piece on the 6. After that, every time it was Kirsty's turn, her die followed the sequence 6, 4, 2, 5, 3, 1; so her first move was to square 6, her second was to square 10, her third was to 12, etc. After his first turn when he threw the 6, Tom's die followed the sequence 2, 4, 6, 1, 3, 5 each time, so his second move was to square 8, his third was to 12, etc. The normal rules of the game were followed, so whenever someone landed on a square that had the foot of a ladder, the piece was moved to the top of the ladder. Whenever someone landed on a square that had the head of a snake, the piece was moved to the tail of the snake. The number thrown to end the game didn't necessarily matter, since the first person to move a piece completely off the board won. Who won the game—Kirsty or Tom?

100	99	98	97	96	95	94	93	92	91
81	82	83	84	85	86	87	88	89	90
80	79	78	77	76	75	74	73	72	71
61	62	63	64	65	66	67	68	69	70
60	59	58	57	56	55	54	53	52	51
41	42	43	44	45	46	47	48	49	50
40	39	38	37	36	35	34	33	32	31
21	22	23	24	25	26	27	28	29	30
20	19	18	17	16	15	14	13	12	11
1	2	3	4	5	6	7	8	9	10

START →

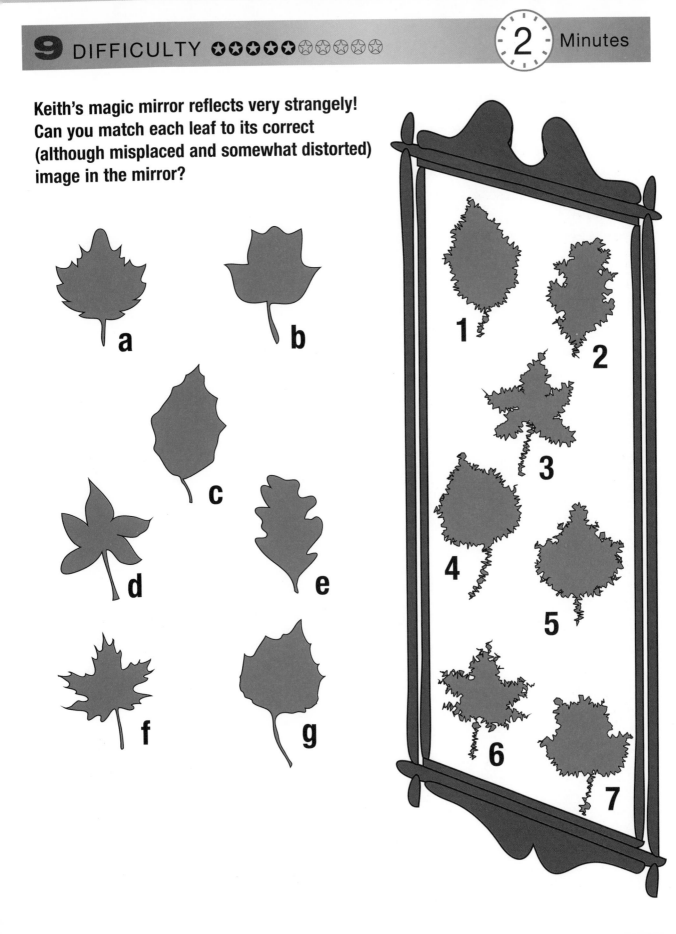

10 DIFFICULTY ✪✪✪✪✪✪☆☆☆☆

In this two-player game, the aim is to make a continuous path in your color across the board. Choose a red or blue pen, then decide who goes first. To begin, the first player draws a line from any dot of his or her color to the nearest dot horizontally or vertically next to it. The second player does the same between two dots of their own color.

Players continue to make moves in turns. Because each player is using his or her own set of dots and paths, there cannot be a tie. Lines must not cross at any point. The winner is the first player to achieve a continuous path in his or her color, from his or her starting side to the opposite edge.

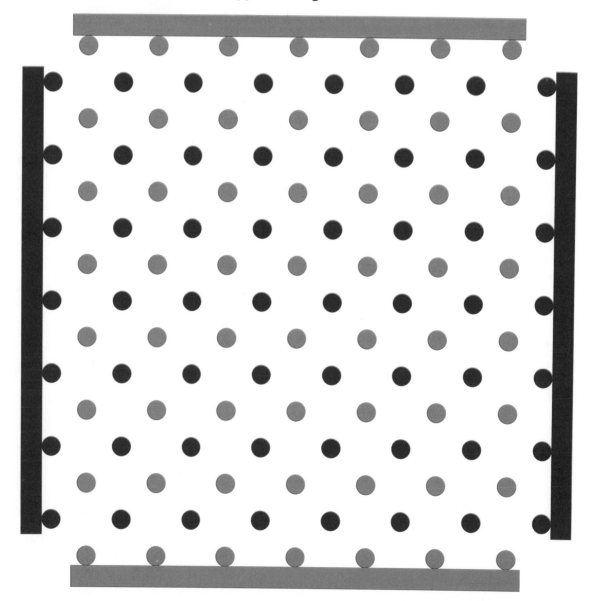

11 DIFFICULTY ✪✪✪✪✪✪✩✩✩✩   ⏱ **8** Minutes

In each of the four buildings below, one type of brick is used more or less frequently than it is in the other three buildings. Can you discover the different brick in each construction? The ten brick types are as follows:

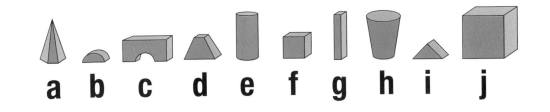

a   b   c   d   e   f   g   h   i   j

Building 1

Building 2

Building 3

Building 4

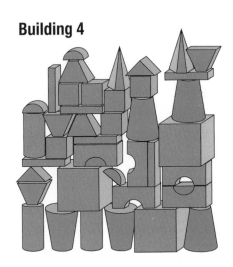

12 DIFFICULTY ●●●●●○○○○○ 3 Minutes

At the local casino, they play a dice gambling game that involves throwing two dice and betting a stake of $12. What are the rules and how much did Gary Gambler win or lose when he threw a 2 followed by a 3? Study the clues below to discover the answer.

1. Gina threw a 4 followed by a 5 and got $6 back, losing $6.

2. Gordon threw a 1 followed by a 5 and broke even, so got $12 back.

3. Graham threw a 1 followed by a 3 and got $24 back, so won $12.

13 DIFFICULTY ●●●●●●●○○○ 4 Minutes

By drawing three straight lines, can you divide this room into five sections, each containing a bed, a storage unit, a table, and two chairs?

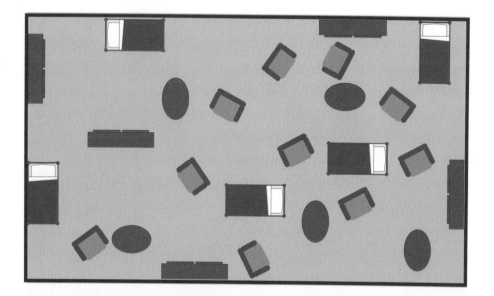

14 DIFFICULTY ✪✪✪✪✪✪☆☆☆☆

⏱ 2 Minutes

A circular loop of string lies flat on a table. Part of the string has been hidden from view by the black border. If X is inside the loop, what can you say about Y? Here's a hint: coloring in some of the areas may help you.

15 DIFFICULTY ✪✪✪✪✪☆☆☆☆☆

⏱ 3 Minutes

Which three pieces can be fitted together to form an identical copy of this shape? Pieces may be rotated, but not flipped over.

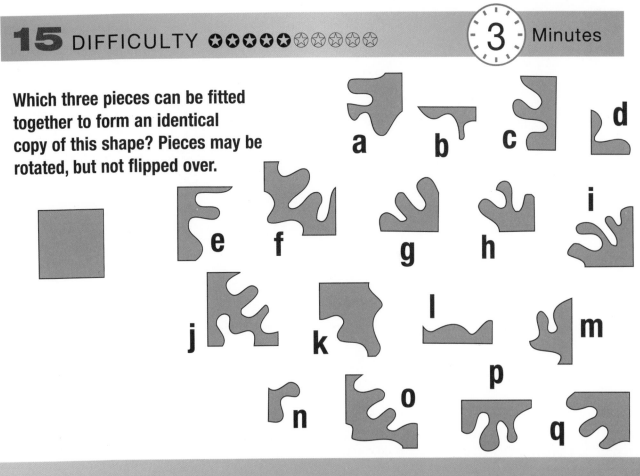

16 DIFFICULTY ✪✪✪✪✪✪✩✩✩✩

4 Minutes

Try to make your way to the center of this circular maze.

17 DIFFICULTY ✪✪✪✩✩✩✩✩✩✩   ⏱ **5** Minutes

Can you spot the eight differences between these two pictures? Circle them in the lower drawing.

MINDW⚙RKS BRAIN TRAINING

18 DIFFICULTY ✪✪✪✪✪✩✩✩✩✩

3 Minutes

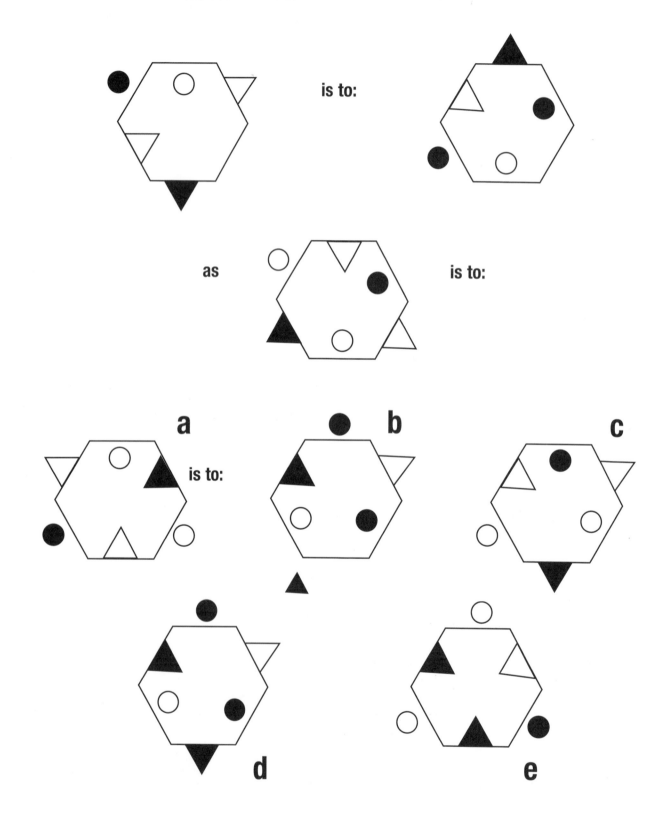

19 DIFFICULTY ✪✪✪✪✪✪☆☆☆☆   ④ Minutes

When the shape below is folded into a cube, which one of the following
(a, b, c, d, or e) is produced?

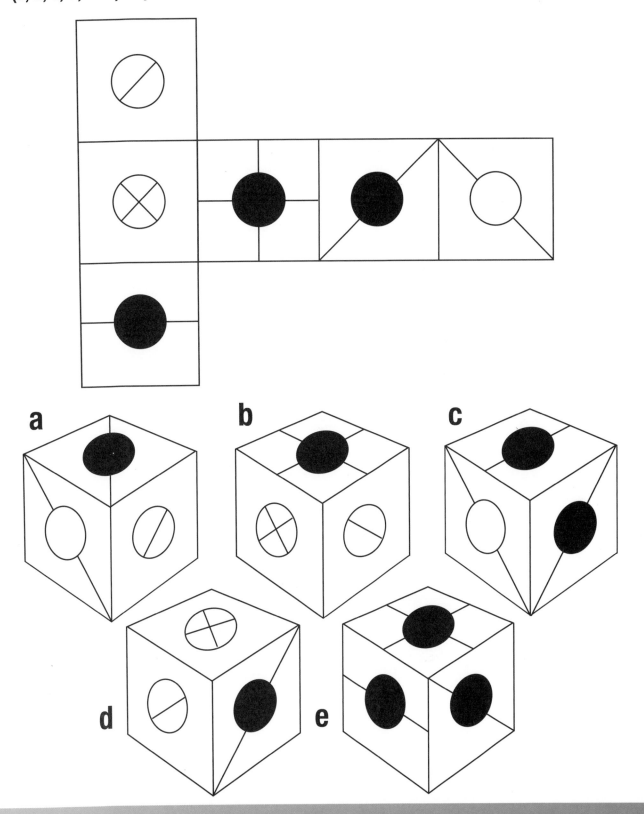

20 DIFFICULTY ★★★★★☆☆☆☆☆   ② Minutes

This cross is hidden only once in the large grid of squares below. The pattern may be rotated but not reflected. Can you find it?

21 DIFFICULTY ✪✪✪✪✪✪✪☆☆☆   30 Minutes

Think deeply and you might find a way to complete this numeropic.

How to do a numeropic:

Along each row or column, there are numbers that indicate how many blocks of black squares are in a line. For example, "3, 4, 5" indicates that from left to right or top to bottom, there is a group of three black squares, then a group of four black squares, then another group of five black squares.

Each block of black squares on the same line must have at least one white square between it and the next block of black squares. Blocks of black squares may or may not have a number of white squares before and after them.

It is sometimes possible to determine which squares will be black without reference to other lines or columns. It is helpful to put a small dot in a square you know will be empty.

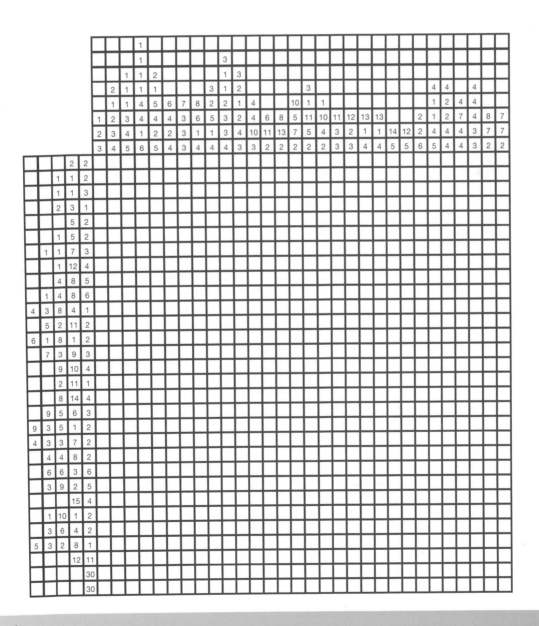

22 DIFFICULTY ★★★★★★☆☆☆☆ ⏱ 5 Minutes

What shape should be in the middle?

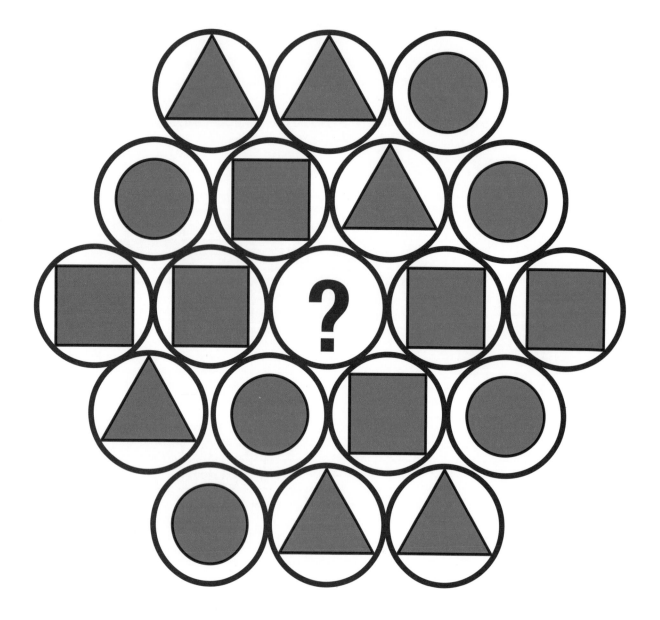

23 DIFFICULTY ✪✪✪✪✪✪✪✪☆☆   6 Minutes

How many differences can you spot between these two pictures, given that one is supposed to be an exact mirror image of the other? Circle them in the drawing on the right.

24 DIFFICULTY ✪✪✪✪✪☆☆☆☆☆   5 Minutes

Using three of the four different mathematical operators (+, −, x, ÷), can you find the correct totals for each of these dice problems?

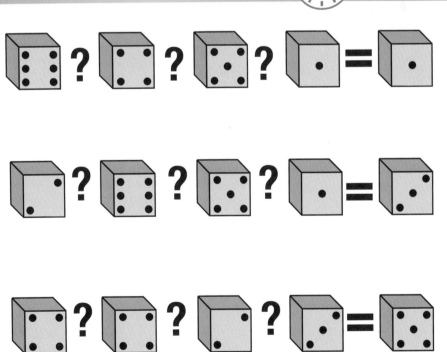

⏱ **5** Minutes

When the shape below is folded into a cube, which one of the following (a, b, c, d, or e) is produced?

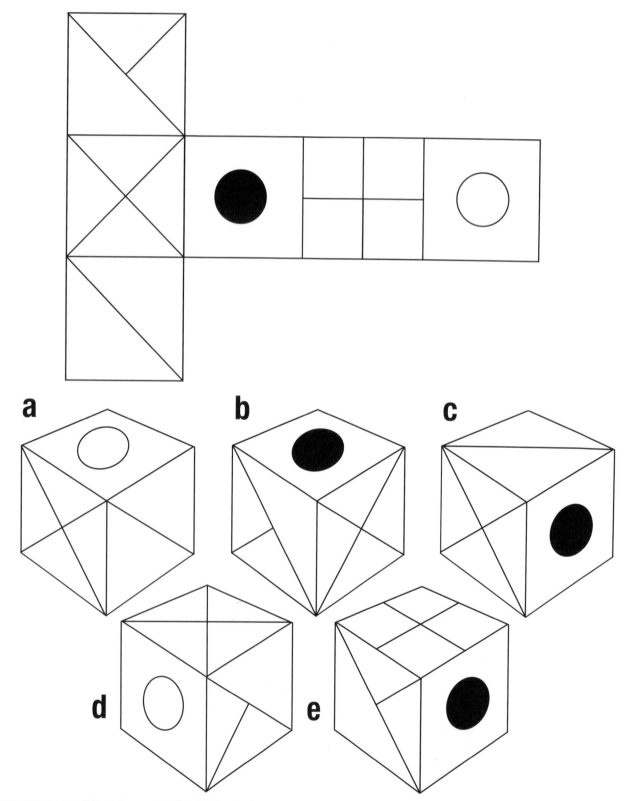

26 DIFFICULTY ✪✪✪✪✪☆☆☆☆☆

1 Minute

Study this picture for one minute, then see if you can answer the questions on the next page.

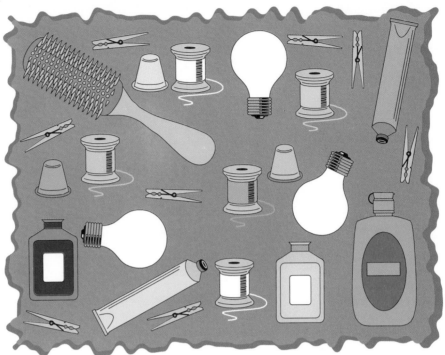

27 DIFFICULTY ✪✪✪✪☆☆☆☆☆☆

2 Minutes

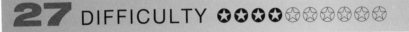

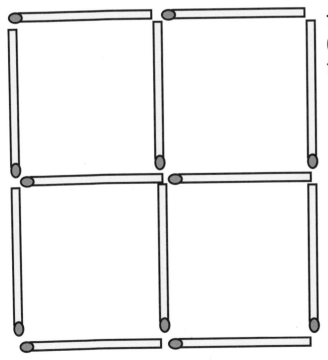

These matches make five squares. Can you move two to make five triangles?

[26] DIFFICULTY ✪✪✪✪✪✪✩✩✩✩✩   ③ Minutes

Can you answer these questions about the puzzle on the previous page without looking back?

1. What color is the hairbrush?

2. How many thimbles appear in the picture?

3. What color is the tube at the top right corner of the picture?

4. How many lightbulbs appear in the picture?

5. How many spools of thread have white thread?

6. How many clothespins appear in the picture?

7. How many bottles have a white label?

8. How many objects are in the picture?

28 DIFFICULTY ✪✪✪✪✪✩✩✩✩✩   ③ Minutes

By drawing three straight lines, can you divide this cloud into four sections, each containing five different symbols?

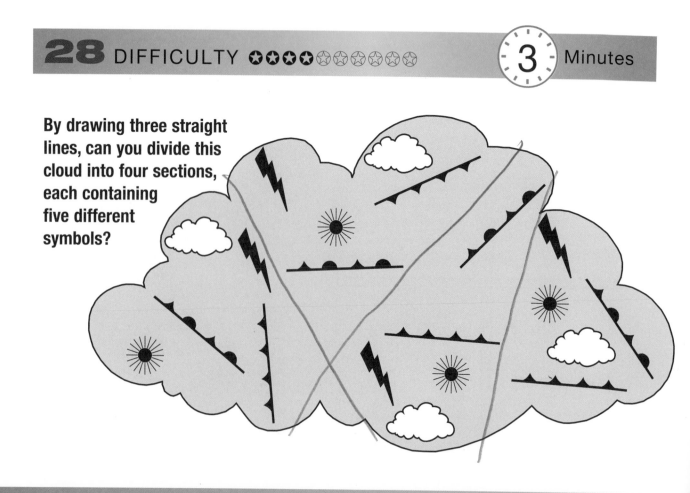

29 DIFFICULTY ✪✪✪✩✩✩✩✩✩ ④ Minutes

Starting at a, see if you can make your way to b in this difficult triangular maze.

2 Minutes

What is the missing shape?

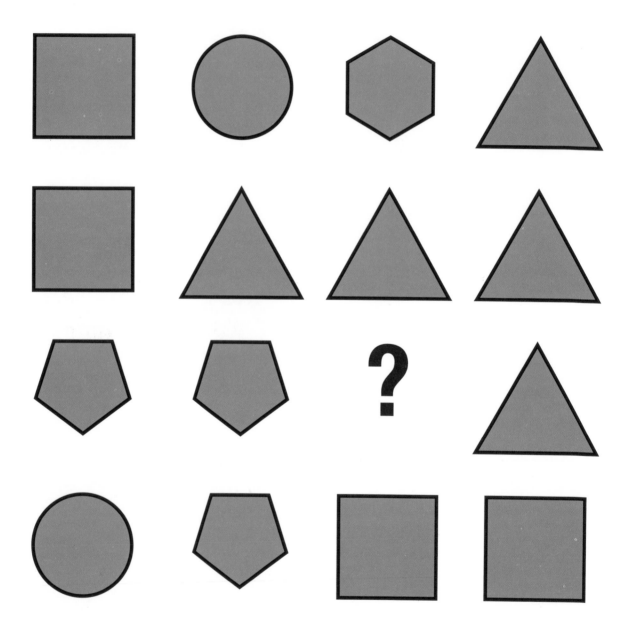

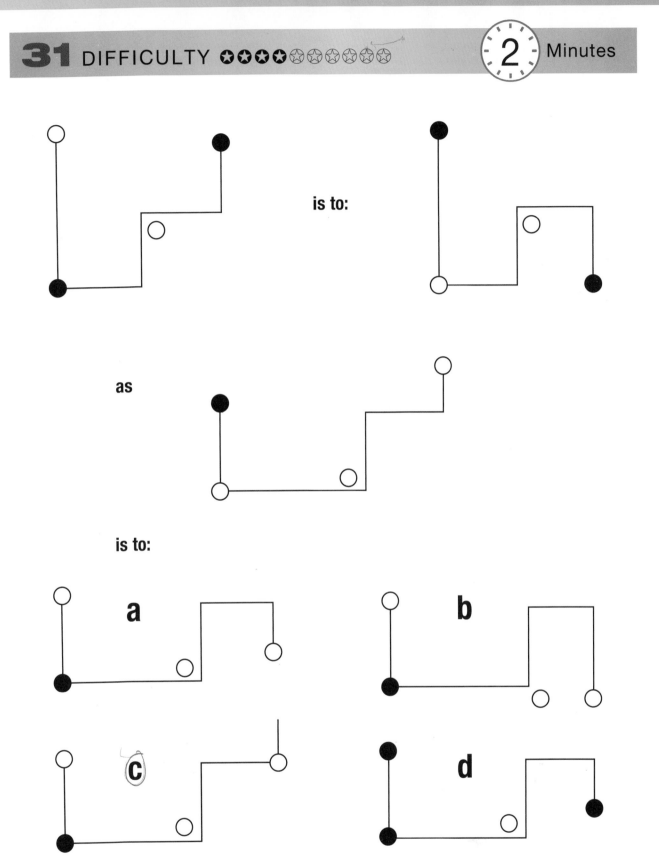

is to:

as

is to:

a

b

c

d

32 DIFFICULTY ★★★☆☆☆☆☆☆☆ ④ Minutes

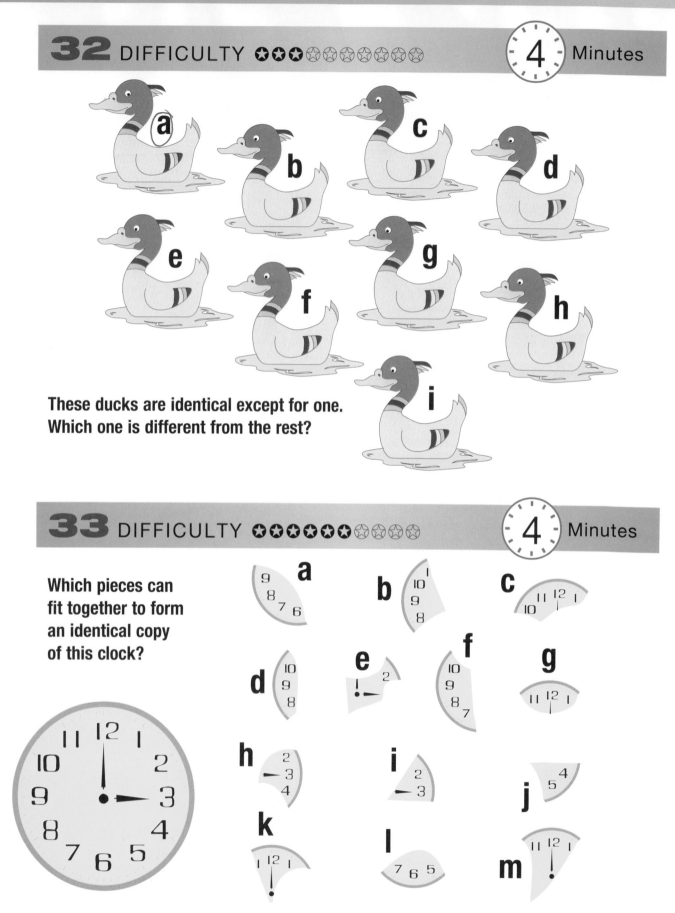

These ducks are identical except for one.
Which one is different from the rest?

33 DIFFICULTY ★★★★★★☆☆☆☆ ④ Minutes

Which pieces can fit together to form an identical copy of this clock?

34 DIFFICULTY ✪✪✪✪✪☆☆☆☆☆   ② Minutes

Study this picture for two minutes, then see if you can answer the questions on the next page.

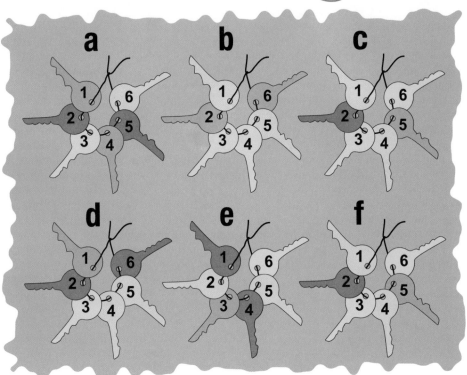

35 DIFFICULTY ✪✪✪✪✪✪☆☆☆☆   ④ Minutes

By drawing three straight lines, can you divide this rectangle into four sections, each containing eight different birds?

[34] DIFFICULTY ✪✪✪✪✪✪✪☆☆☆☆☆   3 Minutes

Can you answer these questions about the puzzle on the previous page without looking back?

1. How many keys are there in total?

2. Which two bunches of keys are identical?

3. How many blue keys appear in total?

4. Which letter identifies the key ring with no red keys?

5. How many keys with the number 6 are yellow?

6. Which letter identifies the key ring with two blue keys touching one another?

7. How many odd-numbered keys are purple?

8. Which letter identifies the only key ring with a purple key numbered 6?

36 DIFFICULTY ✪✪✪✪✪✪✪☆☆☆☆   4 Minutes

Here are ten matches. What is the smallest number you have to take away to leave two?

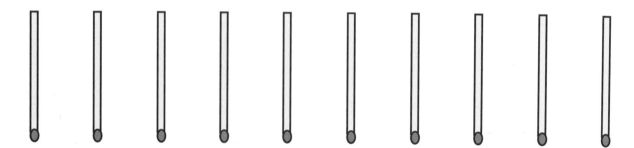

37 DIFFICULTY ✪✪✪✪✪✩✩✩✩✩

2 Minutes

Which number should follow in this dice sequence?

23   14   8   ?

38 DIFFICULTY ✪✪✪✪✪✪✪✪✩✩

5 Minutes

Juliette has lined up these three dice on her coffee table. She can see the same seven faces that you can see. Angelica (her friend, sitting opposite) can see the top three faces of the dice, as well as another four faces you and Juliette cannot see. None of you can see the bottom three faces of these dice. What is the total number of spots on all the faces of the dice that Angelica can see, given that this is a different number from the total number of dots you can see?

39 DIFFICULTY ★★★★★★☆☆☆☆   (30) Minutes

Face facts in order to complete this numeropic. Refer to the instructions on puzzle 21 for help on how to do this kind of puzzle.

Column clues (top):

																				1					2						
											1	1	2										2	5	5	3					
											2	2	1										2	2	2	2					
						1	1	1	1	1	1	1											2	2	2	2					
			1		2	2	1	1	1	2	2							2	2		2	2	2	2	1						
	1	2	1	14	14	7	4	2	9	9	1	1	1	1	1	2	2		2	2	2	2	5	5	3	1					
7	14	2	1	1	1	1	1	1	1	1	2	2	2	2	8	8	8	2	2	2	2	2	5	5	3	1					
3	5	7	3	5	23	5	5	5	11	13	13	13	25	25	25	25	1	9	9	2	2	2	2	5	5	3	1

Row clues (left):

- 15
- 13 6
- 13 7
- 4
- 13 7
- 4 6 6
- 13
- 4 6 6
- 6 6 7
- 6 11 4
- 7 1 9 7
- 19 6
- 20
- 9 7 6
- 20 7
- 5 7 4
- 16 7
- 13 6
- 1 8 2
- 12 2 6
- 1 8 2 7
- 1 8 2 4
- 13 2 7
- 13 2 6
- 14 2
- 14 2
- 14 2
- 7
- 8

David's magic mirror reflects very strangely! Can you match each lamp to its correct (although misplaced and somewhat distorted) image in the mirror?

41 DIFFICULTY ★★★★★☆☆☆☆☆ (4) Minutes

Carefully study the rocking horses below. Which is different from the rest?

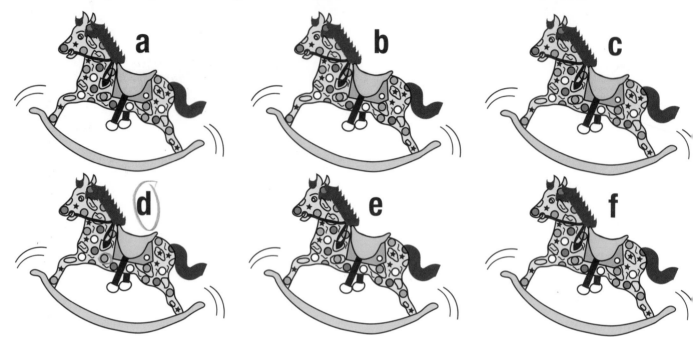

42 DIFFICULTY ★★★★★☆☆☆☆☆ (3) Minutes

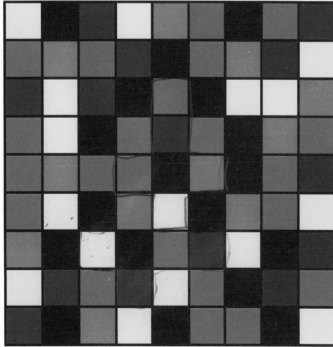

Where can the cross be found in the larger grid? The pattern may be rotated but not reflected.

43 DIFFICULTY ⚹⚹⚹⚹☆☆☆☆☆☆ 4 Minutes

Using three colored pens (e.g., red, yellow, and blue), color in this diagram so that no two bordering areas have the same color.

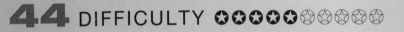

44 DIFFICULTY ⚹⚹⚹⚹⚹☆☆☆☆☆ 5 Minutes

Using straight lines only, can you divide this T-shirt into sections, each containing the same number of differently colored T-shirts?

45 DIFFICULTY ✪✪✪✪✪✪✪☆☆☆   ⏱ **8** Minutes

Starting at the top hexagon in the maze, make your way to the bottom hexagon by moving from shape to adjacent shape. You may ONLY move from a blue shape to a green one, from a green shape to a red one, or from a red shape to a blue one.

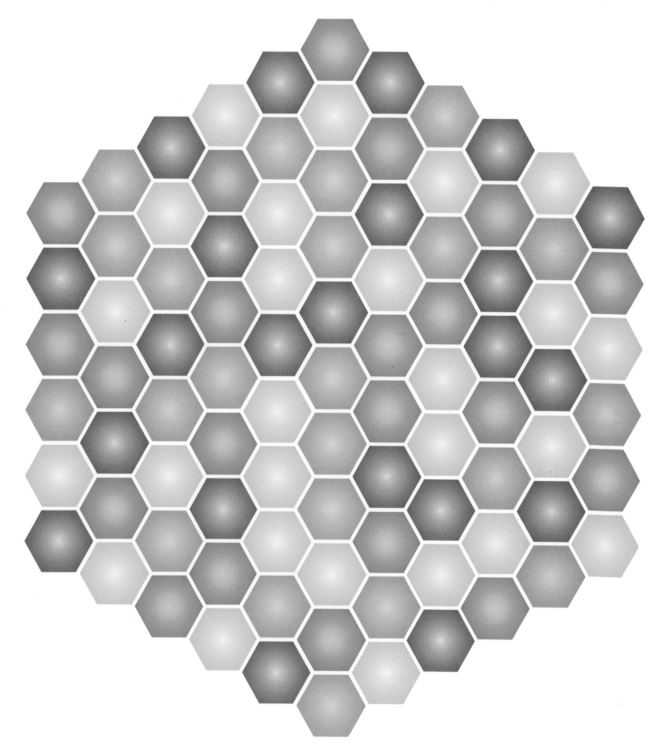

46 DIFFICULTY ✪✪✪✪✪✩✩✩✩✩   (**5**) Minutes

Can you spot the ten differences between these two pictures?
Circle them in the lower drawing.

47 DIFFICULTY ✪✪✪✪✪✪✪☆☆☆   ⏱ **6** Minutes

Mary would like to buy two identical T-shirts for her twin brothers. Which two should she buy?

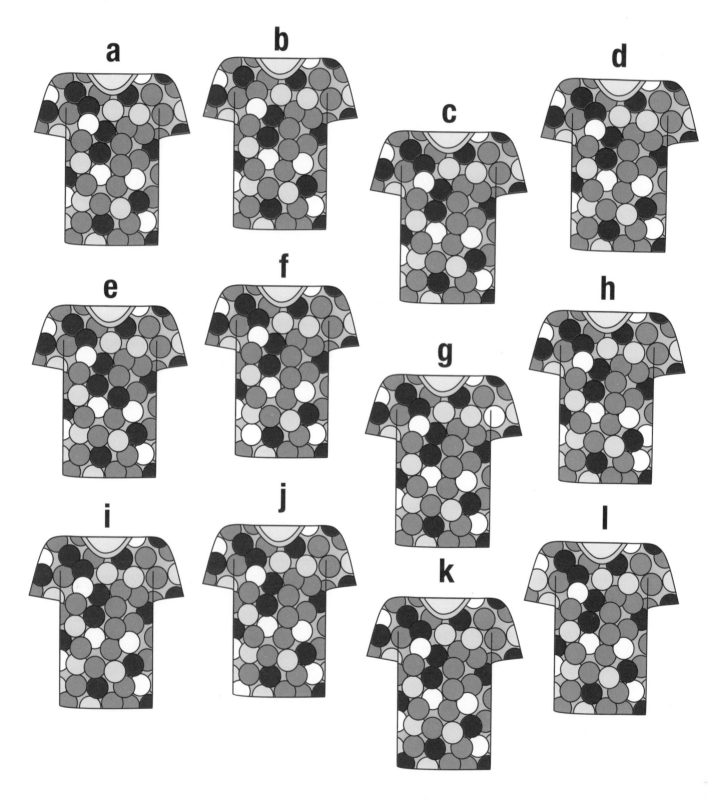

48 DIFFICULTY ⭐⭐⭐⭐⭐☆☆☆☆☆   ⏱ ⑧ Minutes

In each of the four buildings below, one type of brick is used more or less frequently than it is in the other three buildings. Can you discover the different brick in each construction? The ten brick types are as follows:

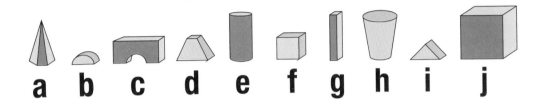

a b c d e f g h i j

Building 1

Building 2

Building 3

Building 4

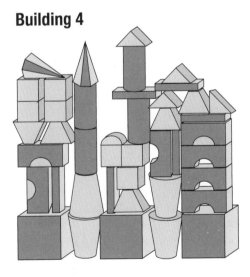

49 DIFFICULTY ✪✪✪✪✪✪☆☆☆☆  4 Minutes

What shape is missing?

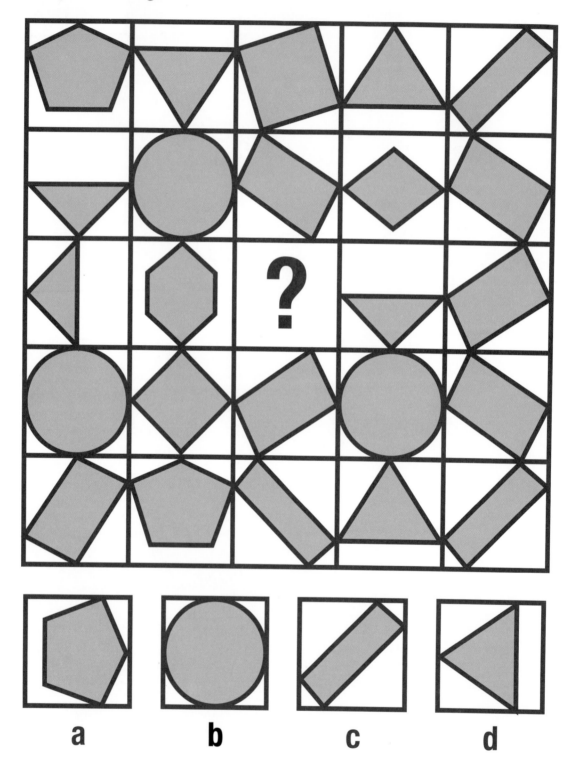

a   b   c   d

50 DIFFICULTY ✪✪✪✪✪☆☆☆☆☆   ⏱ 2 Minutes

Study this picture for two minutes, then see if you can answer the questions on the next page.

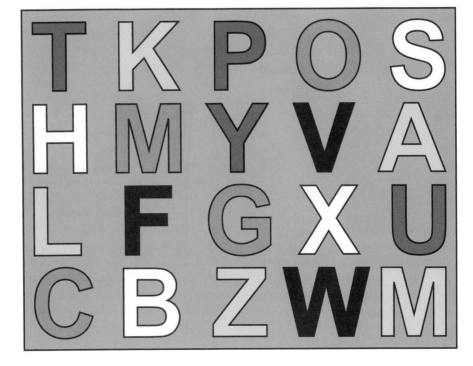

51 DIFFICULTY ✪✪✪✪✪✪☆☆☆☆   ⏱ 2 Minutes

Think laterally to make a perfect square out of these four heptagonal coins.

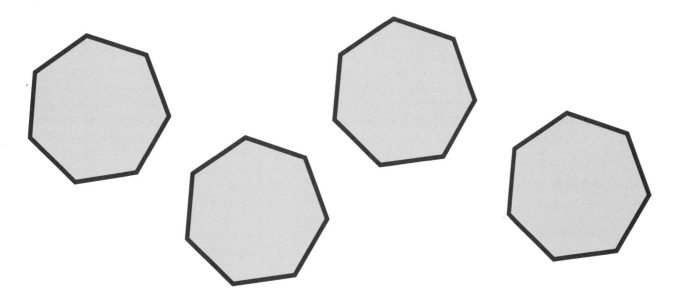

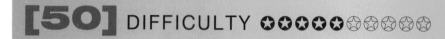

[50] DIFFICULTY ✪✪✪✪✪☆☆☆☆✪ ⏱ (3) Minutes

Can you answer these questions about the puzzle on the previous page without looking back?

1. Which letter appears twice?

2. Which color is used for more letters than any other color?

3. What color is the Y?

4. What color is the letter above the Y?

5. Which letter is directly below the F?

6. Which letter is between the C and the H?

7. What color is the V?

8. Which letter is left of the S?

52 DIFFICULTY ✪✪✪✪✪✪✪✪☆☆ ⏱ (4) Minutes

It is not possible to color in this diagram with just three different pens so that no two bordering areas have the same coloring. Can you manage it by resorting to a fourth color for only one area?

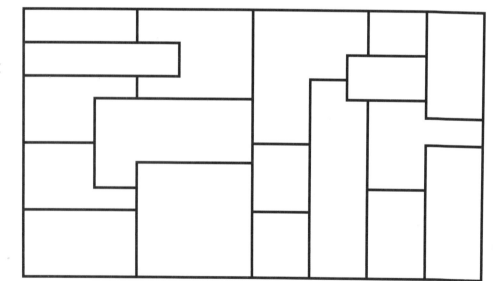

In this two-player network game, all you need to start are three + signs drawn on a piece of paper. The first player connects up any two of the "crossroads" and adds a third + sign somewhere along that route, in effect adding two new spur roads. The second player does the same, making sure that the lines do not cross. The play continues back and forth between both players until no valid move can be made.

The illustration shows the first three moves in a sample game.

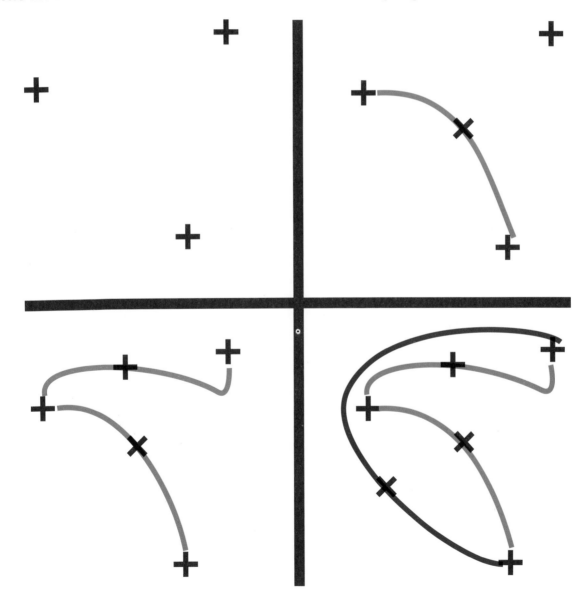

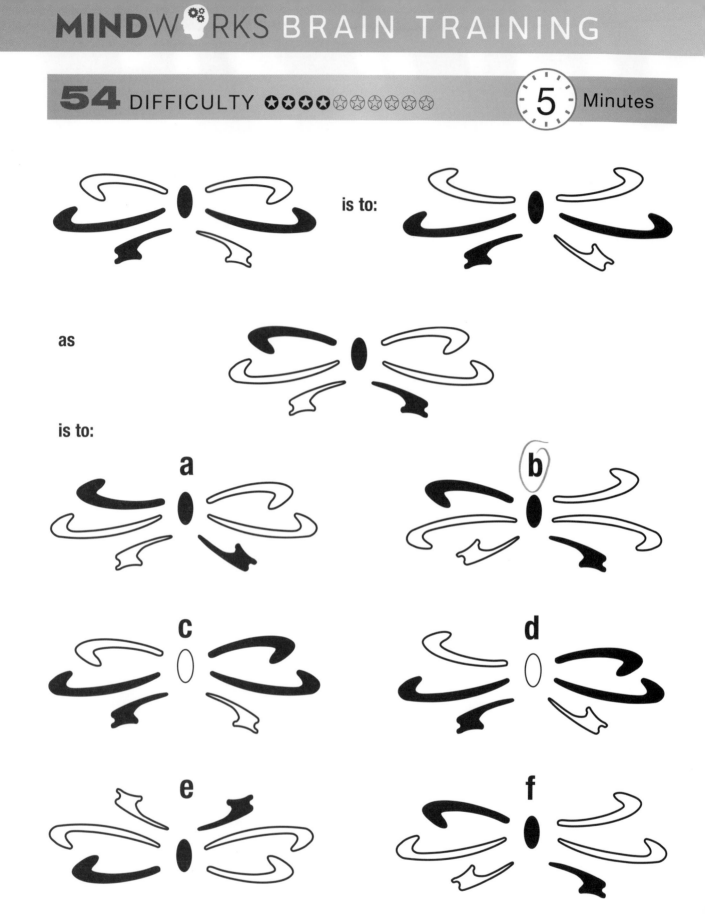

is to:

as

is to:

a

b

c

d

e

f

55 DIFFICULTY ✪✪✪✪✪✪✫✫✫✫ ⏱ 30 Minutes

Make the connections between the numbers to complete this numeropic.
See puzzle 21 for instructions on how to complete this kind of puzzle.

Top clues (columns):

```
                                              3  3
                                    3  3  1  1  3  3
                        4  4  5  4  4  2  2  5  5  2  2  4  4  5  4  4
              6  6     7  4  5  4  5  5  6  5  2  2  5  6  5  5  4  5  4  7
        6  6 12 12  7  6  2  6 10 12 12  6  5  5  5  5  6 12 12 10  6  2  6  7  6  6  6  6
     4  6 11  1  1 17  9  7  5  4  3  3  2  2  1  1  2  2  3  3  4  5  7  9 17 15 15 11  6  4
     6  2  2  2  2  2  2  2  2  2  2  2  2  2  2  2  2  2  2  2  2  2  2  2  2  2  2  2  2  6
```

Left clues (rows):

```
              12
              16
              20
          11  11
           9   9
    7  2   2   7
    7  2   2   7
       7  14   7
       7   6   6   7
       4   2   4
       5   6   5
       4  10   4
       5  12   5
       5  12   5
    4  6   6   4
    4  5   5   4
 4  5  2   5   4
 4  5  2   5   4
    5  5   5   5
    5  6   6   5
       6  12   6
       7  12   7
       8  10   8
       9   6   9
    3  7   2  12
       3   9  14
              30
          1   1
              30
              30
```

56 DIFFICULTY ✪✪✪✪✪✪✪✰✰   ⏱ ③ Minutes

Can you match this potted plant with its shadow?

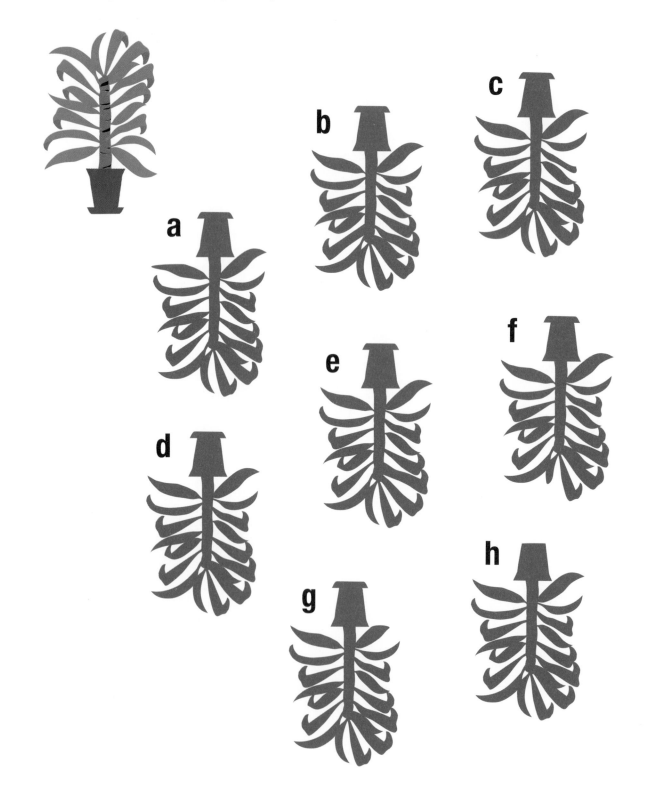

57 DIFFICULTY ✪✪✪✪✪✪✪☆☆  **5** Minutes

Travel from any star on the top row of the grid to any star on the bottom row by moving from one square in the grid to an adjacent one. You may ONLY move from a star to a square, from a square to a circle, or from a circle to a star. You may not move diagonally. Colors are only there to confuse.

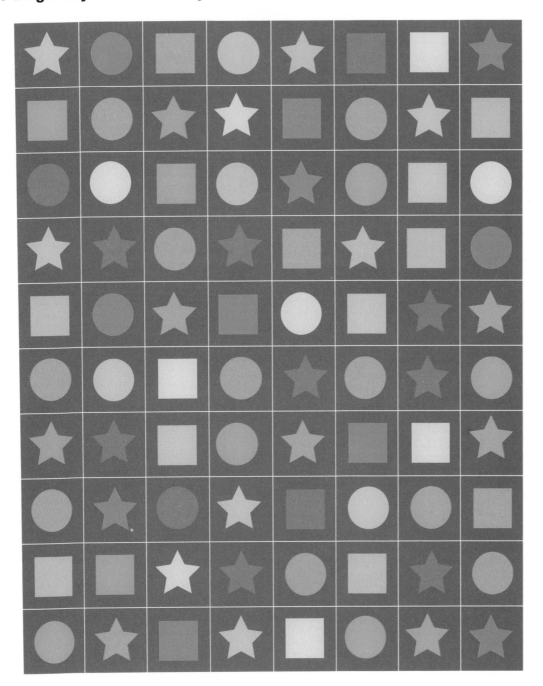

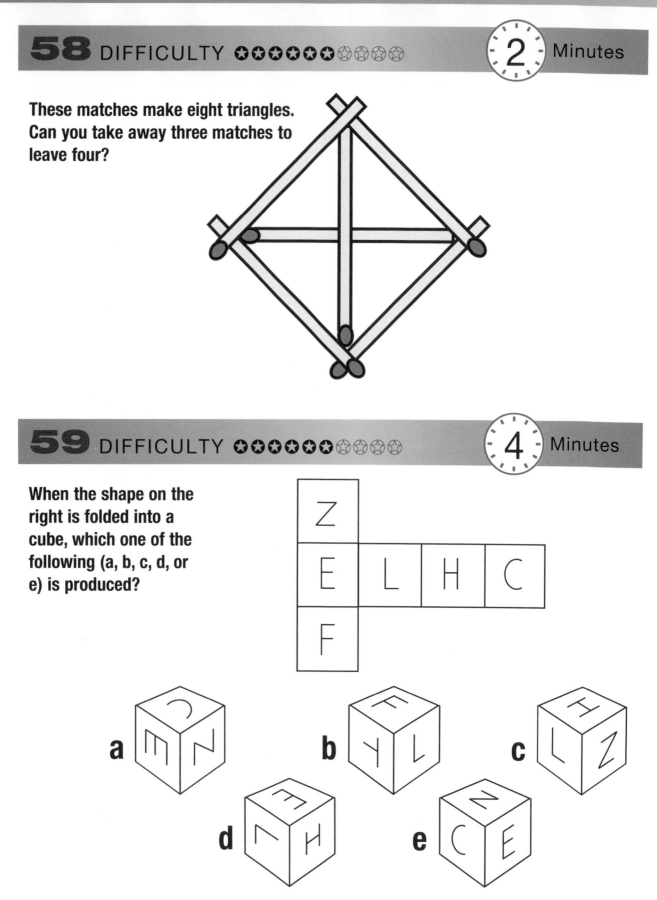

58 DIFFICULTY ✪✪✪✪✪✪✩✩✩✩ ⟨2⟩ Minutes

These matches make eight triangles. Can you take away three matches to leave four?

59 DIFFICULTY ✪✪✪✪✪✪✩✩✩✩ ⟨4⟩ Minutes

When the shape on the right is folded into a cube, which one of the following (a, b, c, d, or e) is produced?

60 DIFFICULTY ●●●●●○○○○○ ③ Minutes

These balls have been kicked around, but all are identical except for one. Which one is different from the rest?

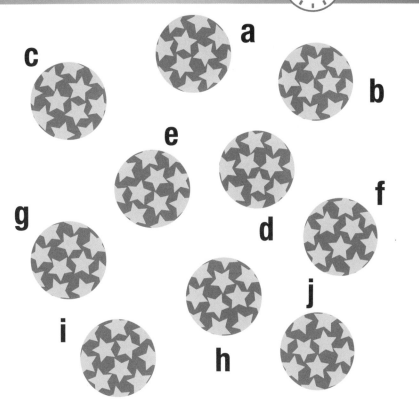

61 DIFFICULTY ●●●○○○○○○○ ⑤ Minutes

Can you spot the ten differences between these two pictures? Circle them in the drawing on the right.

62 DIFFICULTY ✪✪✪✪☆☆☆☆☆☆ | 3 Minutes

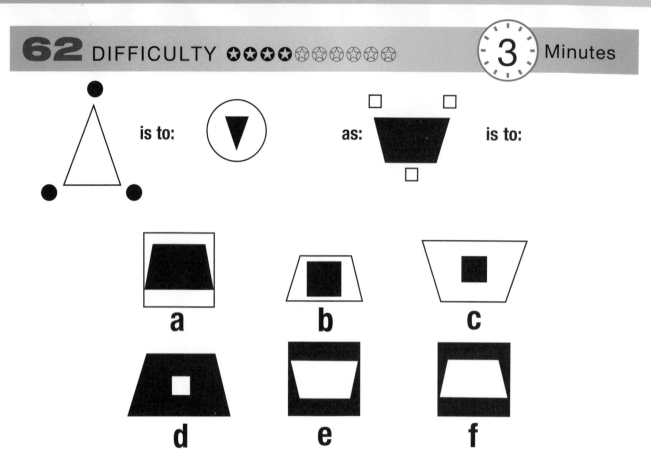

63 DIFFICULTY ✪✪✪✪✪✪✪☆☆☆ | 5 Minutes

At the local casino, they play a dice gambling game, which involves throwing two dice and betting a stake of $6. What are the rules and how much did Gary Gambler win or lose when he threw a 6 followed by a 1? Study the clues below to discover the answer.

1. Gina threw a 3 followed by a 2 and got $2 back, so lost $4.

2. George threw a 2 followed by a 6 and got $8 back, thus won $2.

3. Graham threw a 4 followed by a 1 and got $6 back, so broke even.

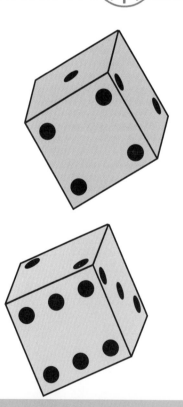

64 DIFFICULTY ✪✪✪✪✪✩✩✩✩✩

⏱ **2** Minutes

Study this picture for two minutes, then see if you can answer the questions on the next page.

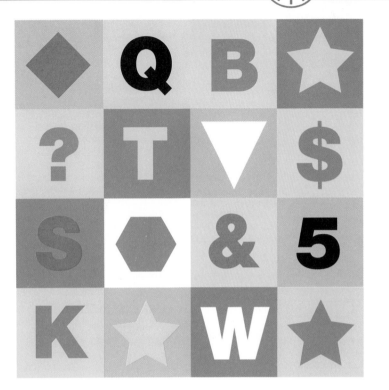

65 DIFFICULTY ✪✪✪✪✪✩✩✩✩✩

⏱ **4** Minutes

Can you pair up these door keys with the imprints of their ends?

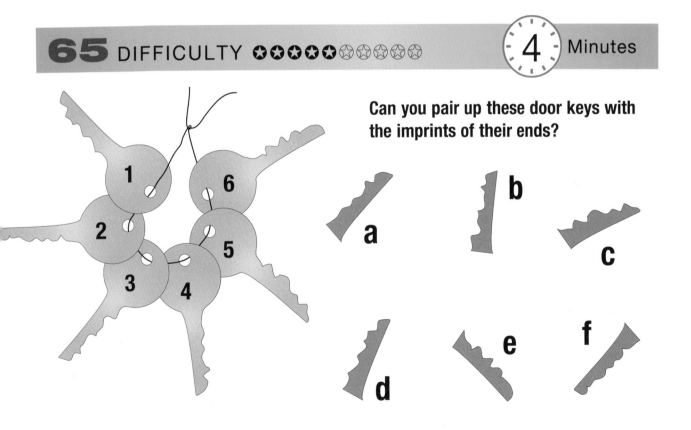

[64] DIFFICULTY ✪✪✪✪✪✪✩✩✩✩✩   ③ Minutes

Can you answer these questions about the puzzle on the previous page without looking back?

1. Which number appears on a square with a blue background?

2. What is the color of the letter K?

3. What color is the question mark?

4. What color is the triangle?

5. Which letter appears above the K?

6. How many letters appear on squares with a green background?

7. How many yellow stars appear in the picture?

8. Which letter appears diagonally between the letter S and the letter B?

66 DIFFICULTY ✪✪✪✪✩✩✩✩✩✩   ③ Minutes

What is the sum total of the spots on the fifteen hidden sides of these four dice?

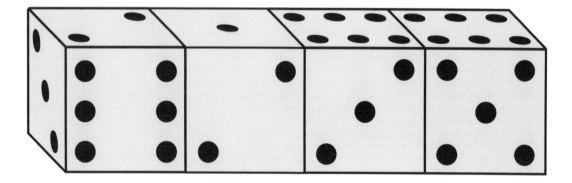

In how many different places can the shape shown be found in the larger grid?
The pattern may be rotated but not reflected.

68 DIFFICULTY ✪✪✪✪✪✪✩✩✩✩✩

10 Minutes

Kirsty played a game of Snakes and Ladders with her brother Tom. He threw the first 6, so started first, placing his playing piece on the 6. After that, every time it was Kirsty's turn, her die followed the sequence 6, 5, 4, 3, 2, 1; so her first move was to square 6, then square 11, etc. After his first turn when he threw the 6, Tom's die followed the sequence 1, 2, 3, 4, 5, 6 each time, so his second move was to square 7, his third was to 9, etc. The normal rules of the game were followed, so whenever someone landed on a square that had the foot of a ladder, the piece was moved to the top of the ladder. Whenever someone lands on a square that had the head of a snake, the piece was moved to the tail of the snake. The number thrown to end the game didn't necessarily matter, since the first person to move a piece completely off the board won. Who won the game—Kirsty or Tom?

100	99	98	97	96	95	94	93	92	91
81	82	83	84	85	86	87	88	89	90
80	79	78	77	76	75	74	73	72	71
61	62	63	64	65	66	67	68	69	70
60	59	58	57	56	55	54	53	52	51
41	42	43	44	45	46	47	48	49	50
40	39	38	37	36	35	34	33	32	31
21	22	23	24	25	26	27	28	29	30
20	19	18	17	16	15	14	13	12	11
1	2	3	4	5	6	7	8	9	10

START →

69 DIFFICULTY ✪✪✪✩✩✩✩✩✩✩  **5** Minutes

Can you spot the ten differences between these two pictures? Circle them in the drawing on the right.

70 DIFFICULTY ✪✪✪✪✪☆☆☆☆☆   ③ Minutes

These witches are identical except for one. Which witch is different from the rest?

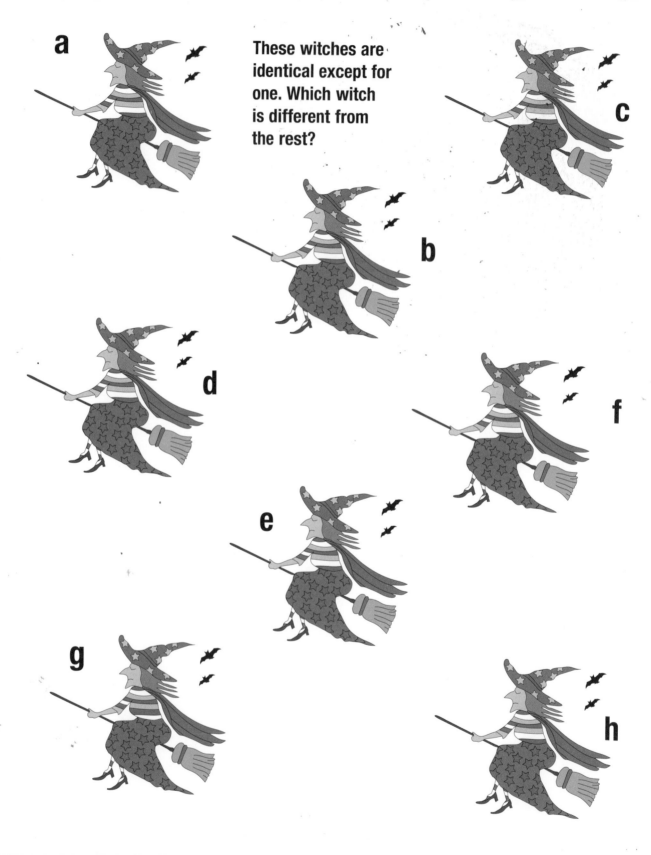

71 DIFFICULTY ✪✪✪✪✪☆☆☆☆☆   6 Minutes

Use four different colored pens to shade in this diagram like a political map so that no two bordering areas have the same color. It's trickier than it looks!

72 DIFFICULTY ✪✪✪✪✪✪☆☆☆☆   3 Minutes

Look carefully—which of the ten clock hands is in the wrong position? Where should it be instead?

73 DIFFICULTY ✪✪✪✩✩✩✩✩✩✩ ④ Minutes

Mrs. R. Teest would like to buy two identical abstract paintings, but is rather confused by the choice at the art gallery. Can you help by finding two that are exactly the same?

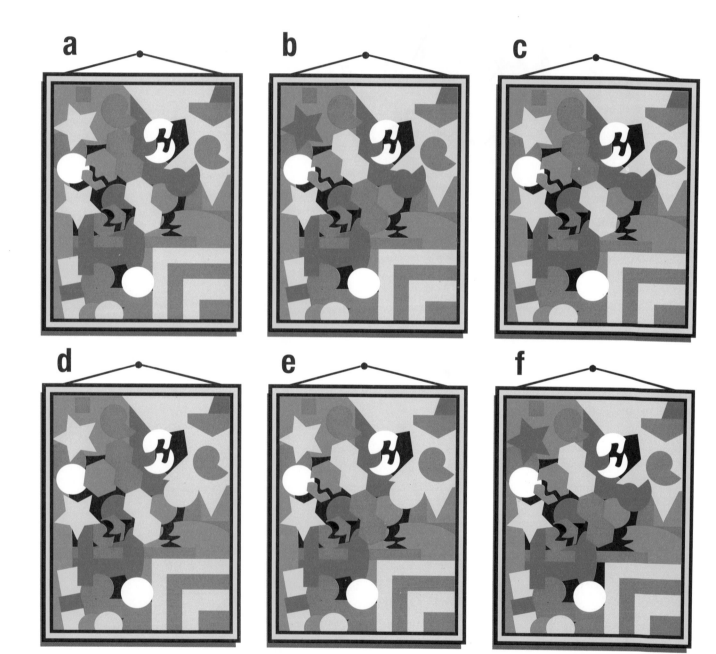

74 DIFFICULTY ✪✪✪✪✪✪✪✩✩✩

3 Minutes

Make your way from A to B collecting just one of each of the four shapes. You can pick them up in any order but you may NOT travel over the same path more than once.

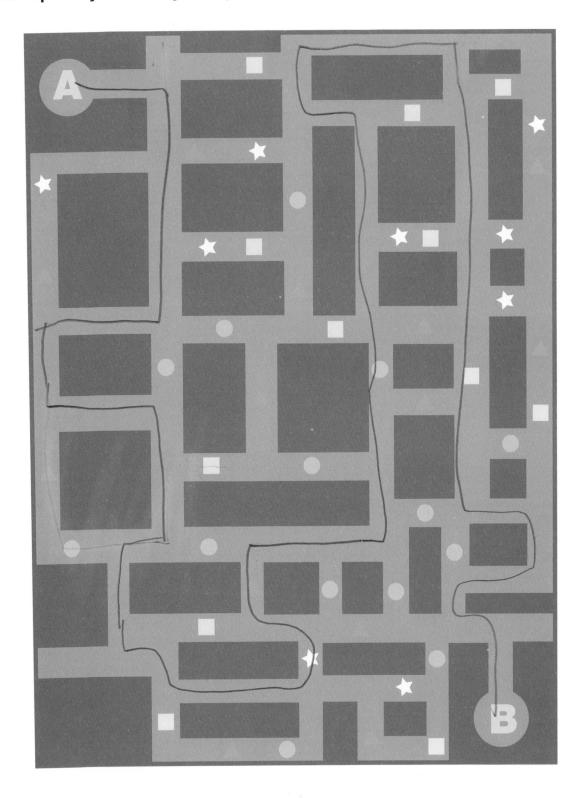

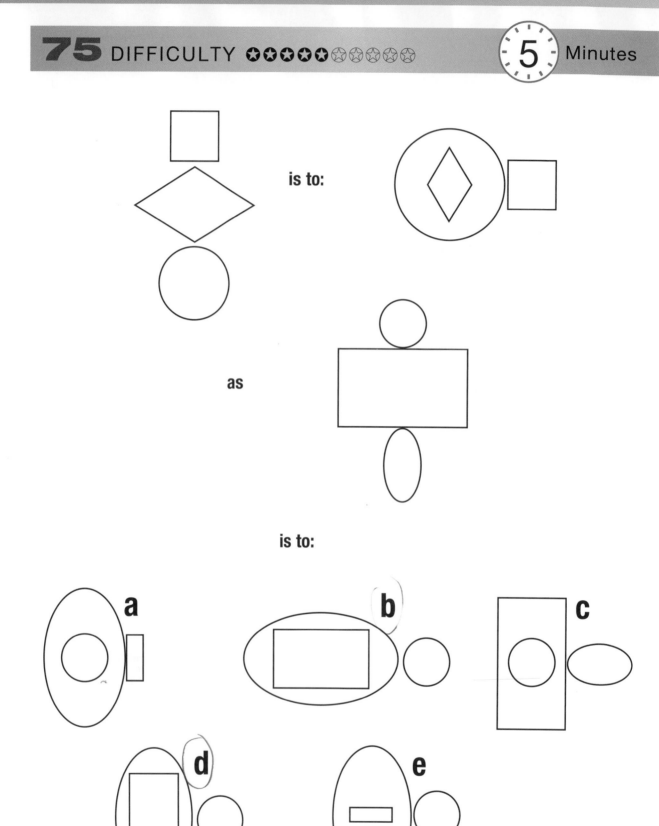

DIFFICULTY ✪✪✪✪✪✩✩✩✩✩　⏱ **6** Minutes

In how many different places can the pattern shown be found in the grid below? The pattern may be rotated but not reflected.

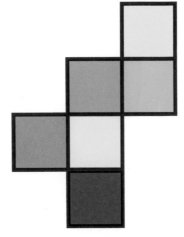

77 DIFFICULTY ★★★★★★☆☆☆☆ ⑳ 30 Minutes

Once you've completed this numeropic, you'll never forget how it's done. See puzzle 21 for instructions on how to complete this type of puzzle.

Column clues (top):

							2																							
							3																							
		1		2	3	3						3													1	2	3			
	3	2	2	1	8	3			3	2	2	3	4	5											1	2	3			
	1	1	2	11	3	1	4		5	3	8	5	8	10	12	20	16	20	20	16	20	19	1	19	16	12	10
3	2	4	17	7	1	1	7	14	19	13	7	5	2	2	2	2	2	3	3	2	2	3	3	19	2	2	1	1	2
1	1	1	1	1	1	1	1	1	2	3	3	3	4	4	1	1	2	2	1	1	2	2	1	1	5	2	2	3	3	2

Row clues (left):

						1	2	1
						2	2	2
					3	2	1	1
						3	2	1
						4	14	2
								18
							5	13
							6	13
						7	2	13
						7	4	12
						3	7	12
						4	7	12
						8	2	13
						8	1	14
					4	4	1	14
				1	2	5	1	14
							8	15
							10	15
						5	5	15
							3	19
				3	4	4	2	4
				2	4	4	2	4
				2	4	4	2	4
2	1	2	1	2	2	1	2	
								2
						2	1	14
						2	15	1
				1	7	2	3	2
					6	2	2	6
								30

78 DIFFICULTY ✪✪✪✪✩✩✩✩✩✩  **6** Minutes

At first glance, these photos may look identical. However, only two are exactly the same. Can you spot them?

a

b

c

d

e

f

79 DIFFICULTY ✪✪✪☆☆☆☆☆☆☆   ④ Minutes

Can you spot the eight differences between these two seasonal pictures? Circle them in the lower drawing.

80 DIFFICULTY ✪✪✪✪✪✪☆☆☆☆   ③ Minutes

Can you rearrange these matches so that the area enclosed is twice as large?

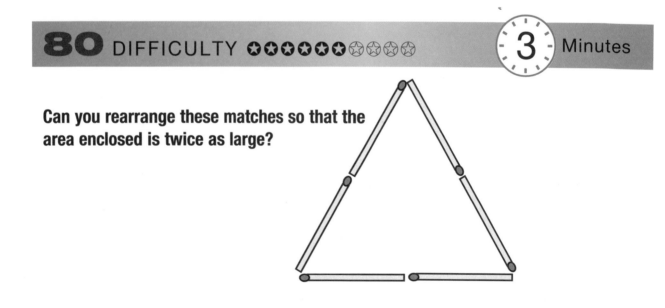

Which of the figures below (a, b, or c) completes the grid above?

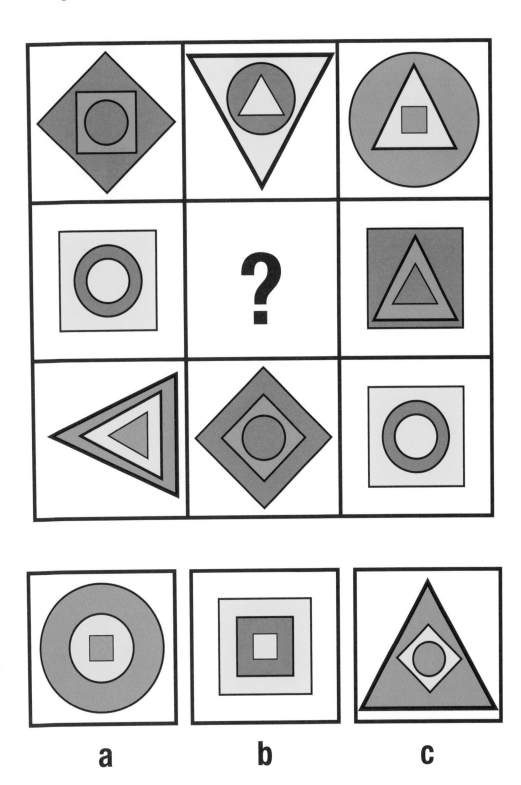

a　　　　b　　　　c

82 DIFFICULTY ★★★★☆☆☆☆☆ ⑤ Minutes

Which three pieces can fit together to match the chair on the right? Any piece may be rotated, but not flipped over.

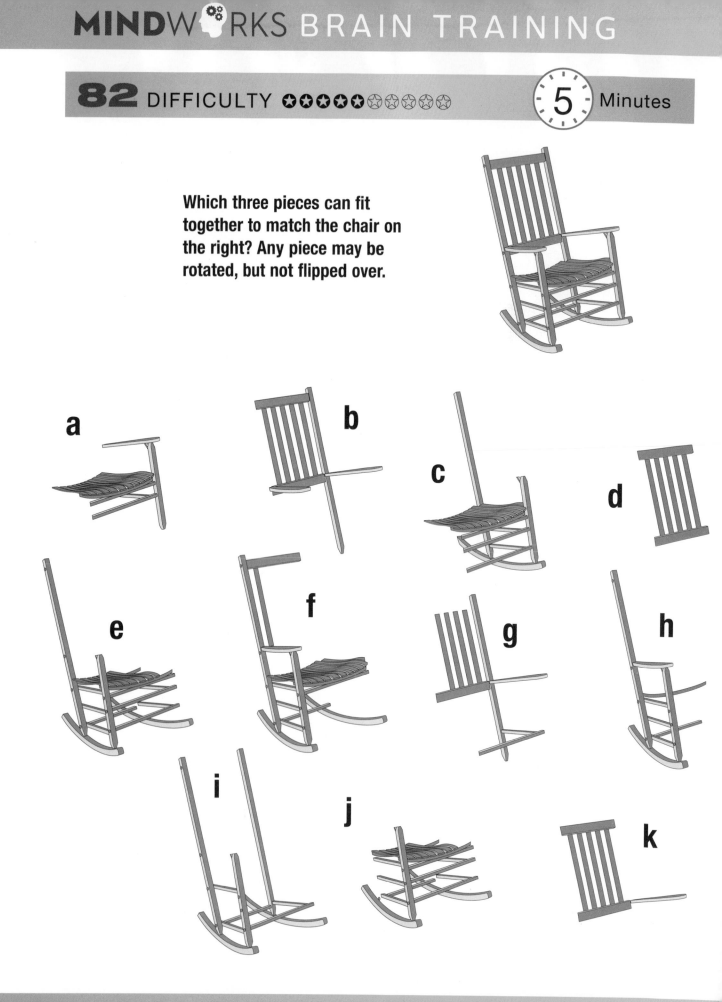

83 DIFFICULTY ✪✪✪✪✪✪☆☆☆☆

4 Minutes

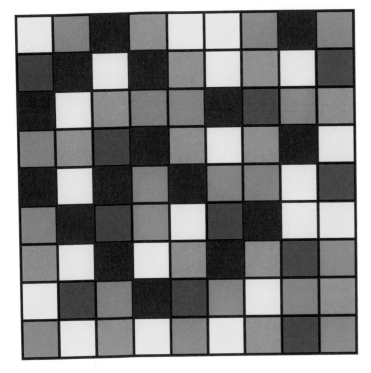

Where can this specific pattern of squares be found in the larger grid? The pattern may be rotated but not reflected.

84 DIFFICULTY ✪✪✪✪✪☆☆☆☆☆

4 Minutes

Arrange these fourteen coins into seven lines of four coins each.

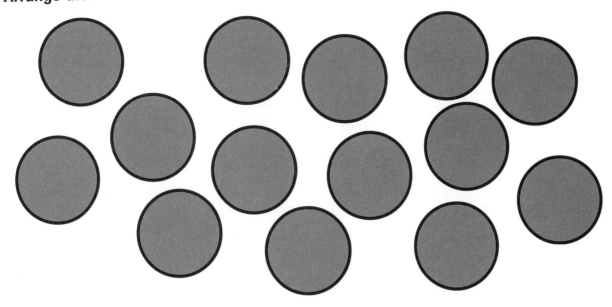

85 DIFFICULTY ★★★★★☆☆☆☆☆ | 3 Minutes

By drawing four straight lines, can you divide this shape into five sections, each containing seven letters?

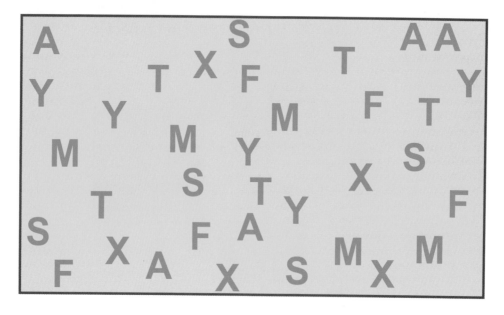

86 DIFFICULTY ★★★★☆☆☆☆☆☆ | 3 Minutes

All of these aliens are odd, but which is the odd one out?

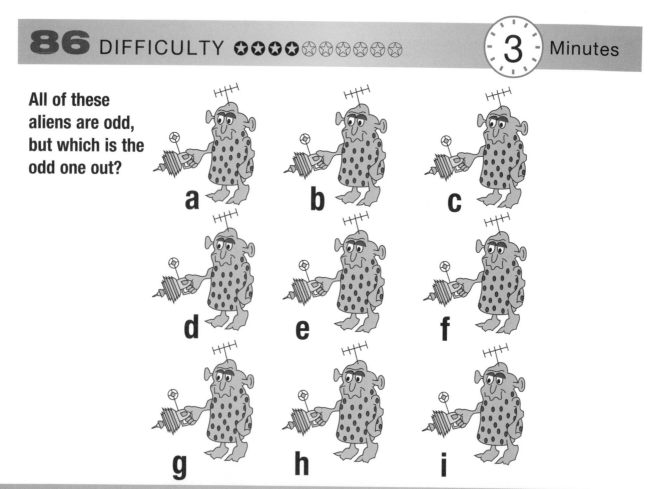

87 DIFFICULTY ★★★★★☆☆☆☆☆   ② Minutes

Study this picture for two minutes, then see if you can answer the questions on the next page.

88 DIFFICULTY ★☆☆☆★☆☆☆☆   ③ Minutes

Which number should follow next in this dice sequence?

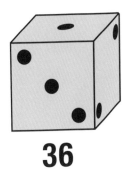

36

12

4

?

[87] DIFFICULTY ✪✪✪✪✪✪✩✩✩✩ ③ Minutes

Can you answer these questions about the puzzle on the previous page without looking back?

1. How many white-petaled flowers have white centers?

2. How many blue-petaled flowers appear in total?

3. How many blue-petaled flowers have blue centers?

4. What color petals does the flower at the very tip of the leaf have?

5. How many red-petaled flowers have yellow centers?

6. How many white-petaled flowers appear in total?

7. What is the total number of flowers in the picture?

8. How many petals does each flower have?

89 DIFFICULTY ✪✪✪✪✪✪✪✩✩✩ ⑥ Minutes

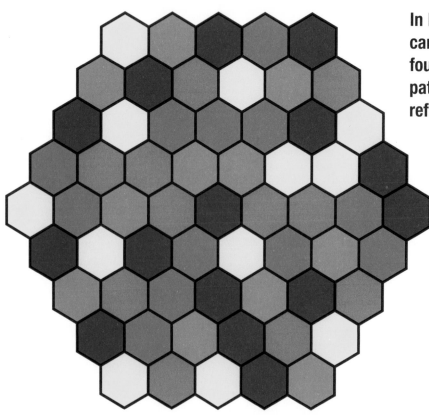

In how many different places can the pattern shown be found in the larger grid? The pattern may be rotated but not reflected.

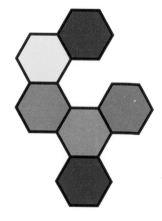

90 DIFFICULTY ✪✪✪✩✩✩✩✩✩✩   ④ Minutes

Can you draw appropriate-colored lines from dot to dot (e.g., a yellow line from yellow dot to yellow dot) so that all the pairs of dots are connected up? None of the colored lines may cross or touch, even at a corner.

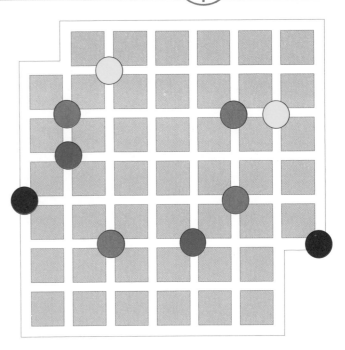

91 DIFFICULTY ✪✪✪✪✪✪✩✩✩✩   ④ Minutes

When this shape is folded to form a cube, which is the only one of the following that can be produced?

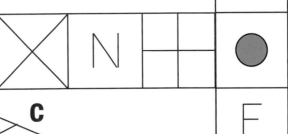

a   **b**   **c**

d   **e**

92 DIFFICULTY ✪✪✪✪✪✪✪✪✪✩ ⏱ **7** Minutes

Can you match the picture of gardening tools and a wheelbarrow with its silhouette?

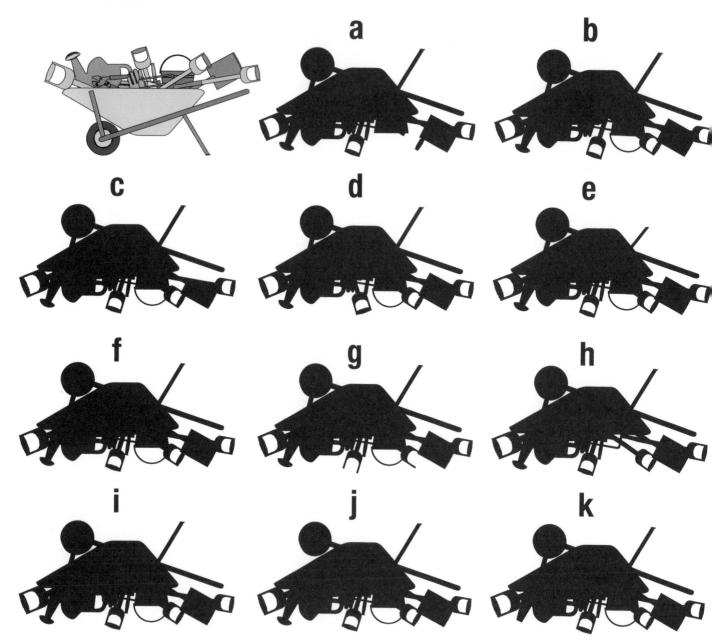

93 DIFFICULTY ✪✪✪✪✪✪✪✪✪✪   ② Minutes

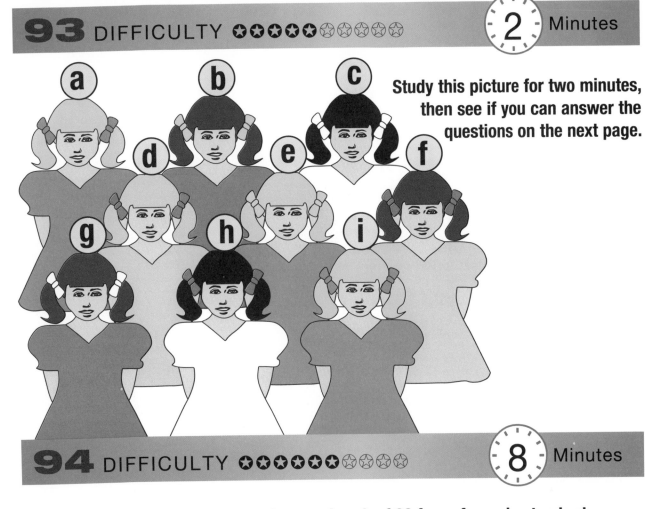

Study this picture for two minutes, then see if you can answer the questions on the next page.

94 DIFFICULTY ✪✪✪✪✪✪✪✪✪✪   ⑧ Minutes

The square below contains exactly one of each of 36 faces from six standard dice. In each horizontal row of six smaller squares and each vertical column of six smaller squares, there are faces with different numbers of spots. There is no die face with five spots in the long diagonal line of six smaller squares running from top left to bottom right, and the total number of spots in this line adds up to 18. The total number of spots in the diagonal line of six smaller squares running from top right to bottom left also adds up to 18. We've placed a few to give you a start, but can you place the rest?

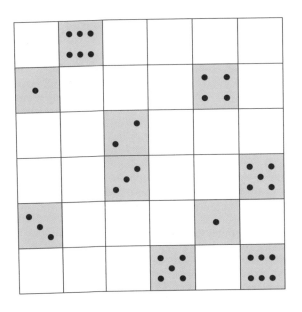

[93] DIFFICULTY ✪✪✪✪✪☆☆☆☆☆   ③ Minutes

Can you answer these questions about the puzzle on the previous page without looking back?

1. How many girls are pictured?

2. How many girls have blond hair?

3. Which girls have pink bows in their hair?

4. How many girls with black hair are wearing white dresses?

5. How many girls with yellow bows are wearing a blue dress?

6. How many girls are wearing pink dresses?

7. Which girl is wearing a white dress and has white bows in her hair?

8. Which girls have the same color hair, dress, and bow?

95 DIFFICULTY ✪✪✪✪✪☆☆☆☆☆   ③ Minutes

One of these shopping baskets is different from the rest. Which is the odd one out?

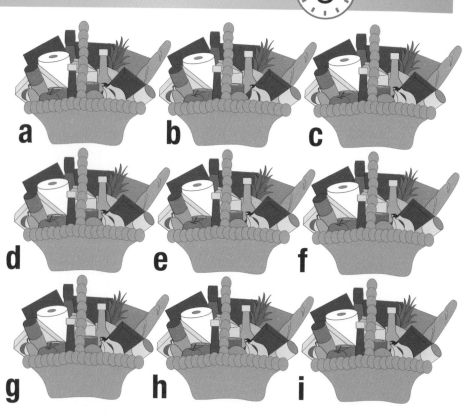

a   b   c

d   e   f

g   h   i

5 Minutes

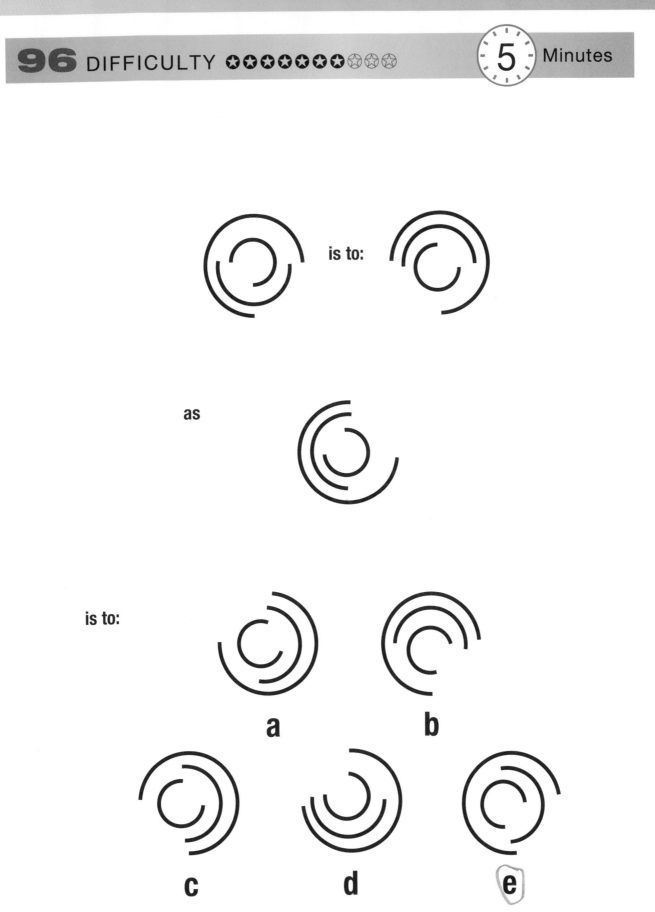

is to:

as

is to:

a

b

c

d

e

97 DIFFICULTY ✪✪✪✪✪✪✪☆☆   5 Minutes

Using the mortar lines, can you get from anywhere on the top of the wall
to anywhere on the bottom?

98 DIFFICULTY ✪✪✪✪✪✩✩✩✩✩ ⏱ ② Minutes

One of these stamps is different from the rest. Which is the odd one out?

a

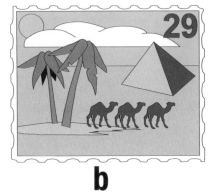

b

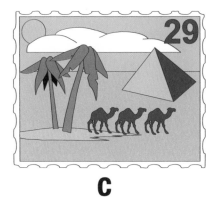

c

d

e

f

g

h

i

99 DIFFICULTY ✪✪✪✪✪✪✪✪☆☆   ⏱ (3) Minutes

Jimmy's magic mirror reflects very strangely!
Can you match each teapot to its correct
(although misplaced and somewhat distorted)
image in the mirror?

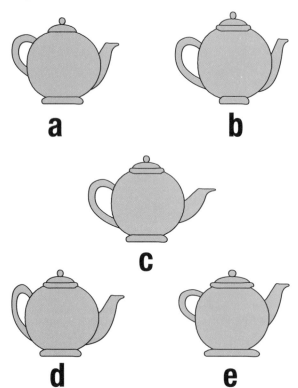

a   b

c

d   e

f   g

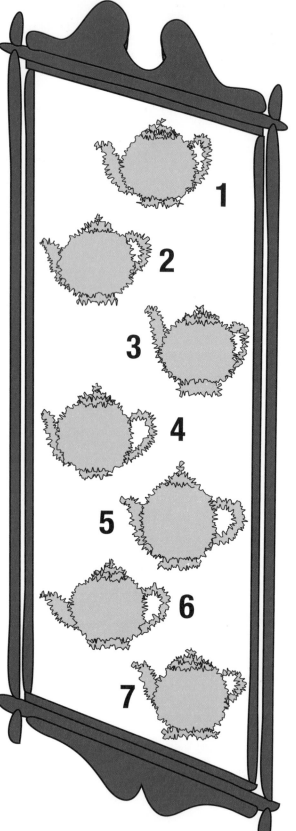

100 DIFFICULTY ✪✪✪✪✪✪✪✪☆☆   5 Minutes

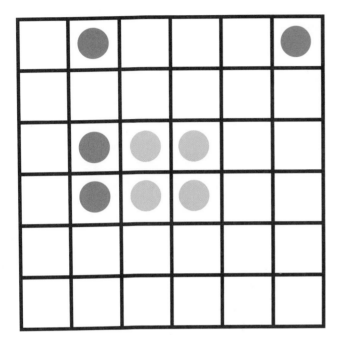

Can you divide this grid into four identical sections, each containing a red and a blue circle?

101 DIFFICULTY ✪✪✪✪✪✪☆☆☆☆   7 Minutes

The square below contains exactly one of each of 36 faces from six standard dice. In each row, each column, and each main diagonal of smaller squares, there are faces with different numbers of spots. We've placed a few to give you a start, but can you place the rest?

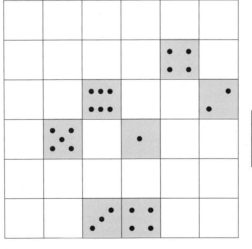

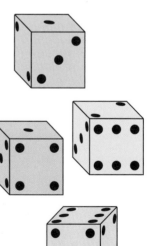

102 DIFFICULTY ✪✪✪✪✪✪✪☆☆☆   ⑤ Minutes

Can you spot the nine differences between these two pictures? Circle them in the lower drawing.

103 DIFFICULTY ★★★★★★☆☆☆☆   ③ Minutes

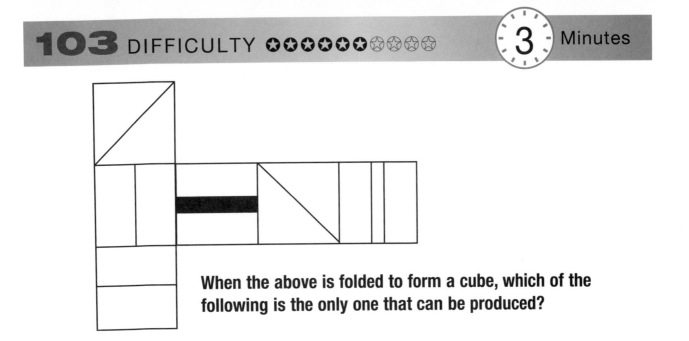

When the above is folded to form a cube, which of the following is the only one that can be produced?

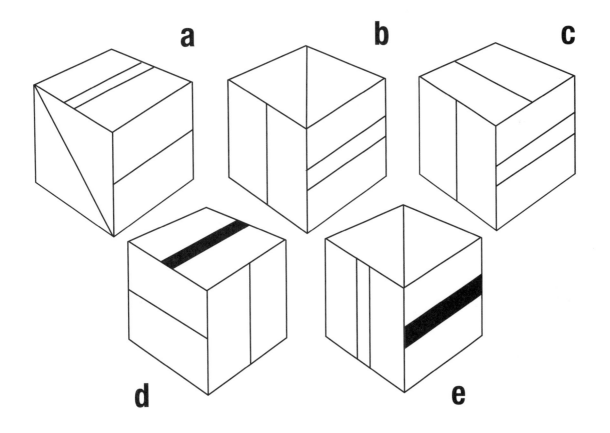

a

b

c

d

e

104 DIFFICULTY ✪✪✪✪✪✪✩✩✩✩

In this two-player network game, the players play on a grid of 5 x 6 or 6 x 5 dots as illustrated. Each player takes a turn to draw a short line between any two dots of his or her color. Play continues until neither player can make a valid move. Lines must not cross. The winner is the player who makes the longest network—in other words, the contiguous network with the largest number of lines between dots. In the example illustrated, the red player won by 29 lines to 13.

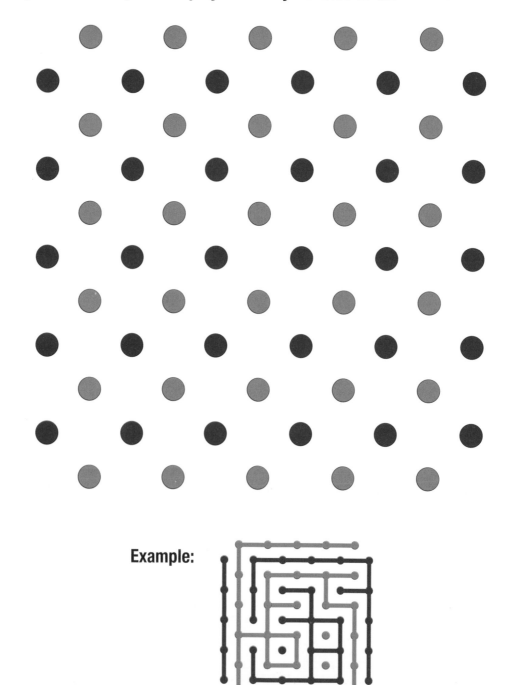

Example:

105 DIFFICULTY ✪✪✪✪✪✪✩✩✩✩ ⏱ (5) Minutes

Which of the four boxed figures (a, b, c, or d) completes the set?

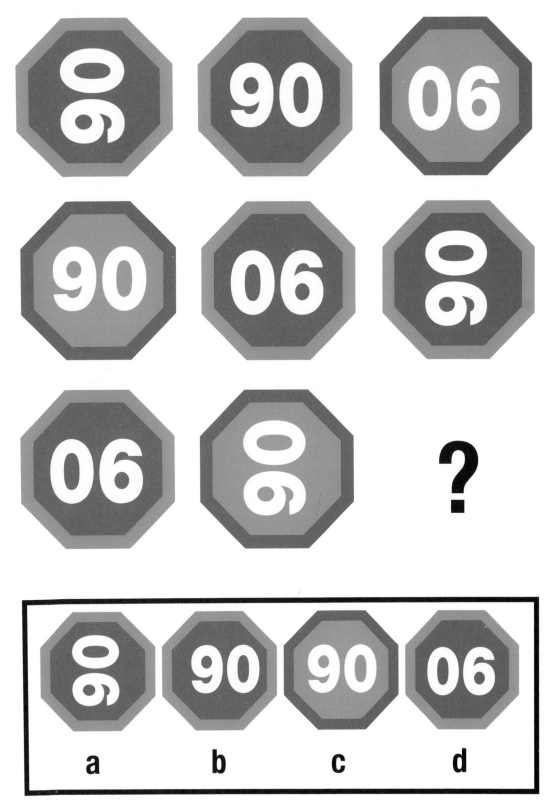

a   b   c   d

106 DIFFICULTY ✪✪✪✪✪✪✪✪☆☆

⏱ **5** Minutes

Which two vases are identical?

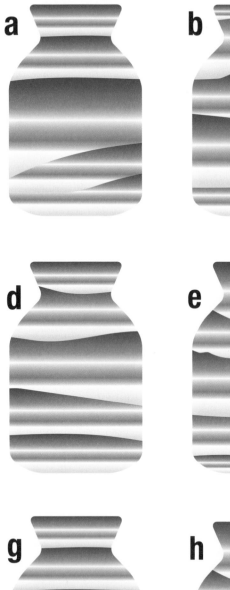
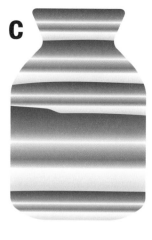

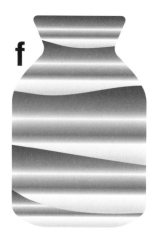
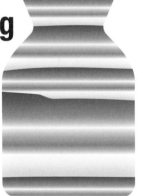

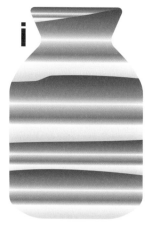

107 DIFFICULTY ✪✪✪✪✪✪✪☆☆☆   ⏱ **5** Minutes

Jimmy's magic mirror reflects very strangely! Can you match each bottle of juice to its correct (although misplaced and somewhat distorted) image in the mirror?

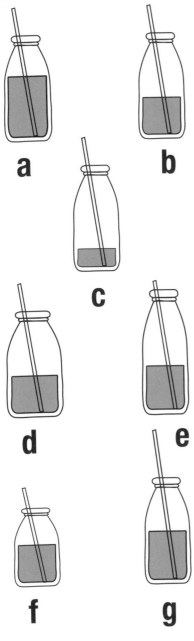

a

b

c

d

e

f

g

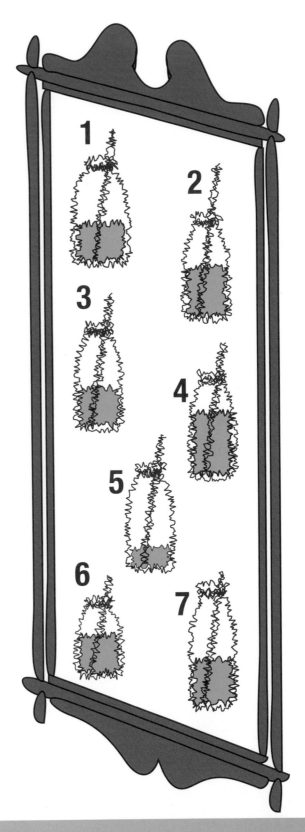

1

2

3

4

5

6

7

108 DIFFICULTY ✪✪✪✪✪✪✪✪☆ | 6 Minutes

Can you spot the eight differences between these two quilts? You may find this a little more difficult because the bottom quilt has been rotated. Mark the changes with an X in the lower quilt.

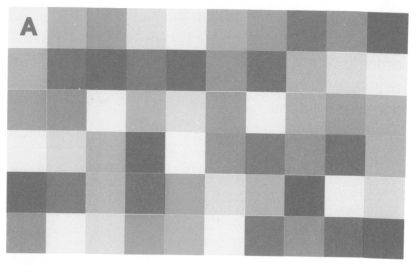

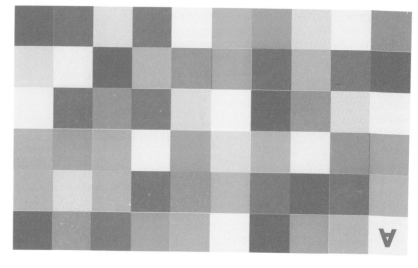

109 DIFFICULTY ✪✪✪✪✪✪☆☆☆☆ | 5 Minutes

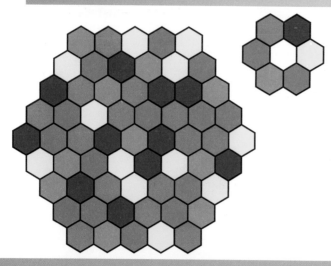

Where can this specific ring of hexagons be found in the larger grid? The pattern may be rotated but not reflected.

110 DIFFICULTY ✪✪✪✪✪✪✩✩✩✩

The aim of this two-player game is to be the first to get four of your symbols in a line (horizontally, vertically, or diagonally). Unlike tic-tac-toe, both players choose a square at the same time by writing down their choice in secret. They then compare notes. If they chose different squares, they put their chosen player symbol in their chosen square. If the squares opted for happen to be the same, players have to vote again and must choose a different square.

There is one special rule: If a player has just one possibility of winning the game on the next move, he or she must go somewhere else and his opponent MUST choose that square instead. For example, in the game illustrated, it is obvious the Circle player would vote for d4 next to try to win the game. Therefore, the Star player must move to d4 and the Circle player must choose somewhere else. It is not necessary to write down the choices for this rule. This rule may seem unfair, but it saves time.

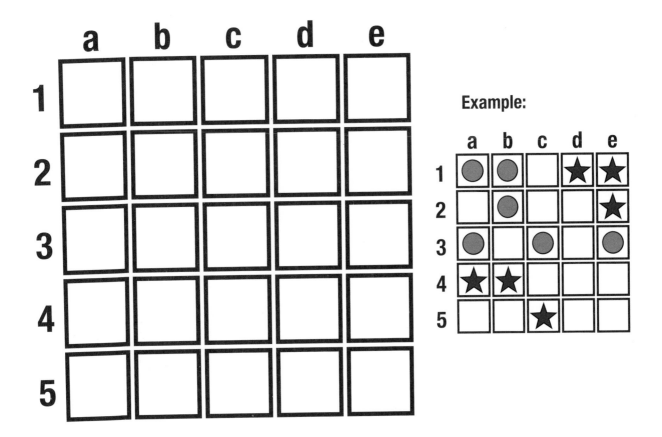

Example:

111 DIFFICULTY ✪✪✪✪✪✪✪☆☆

4 Minutes

Farmer Giles would like to buy two identical tractors. Can you help him? The two that are the same might even be reflections of one another, so look carefully!

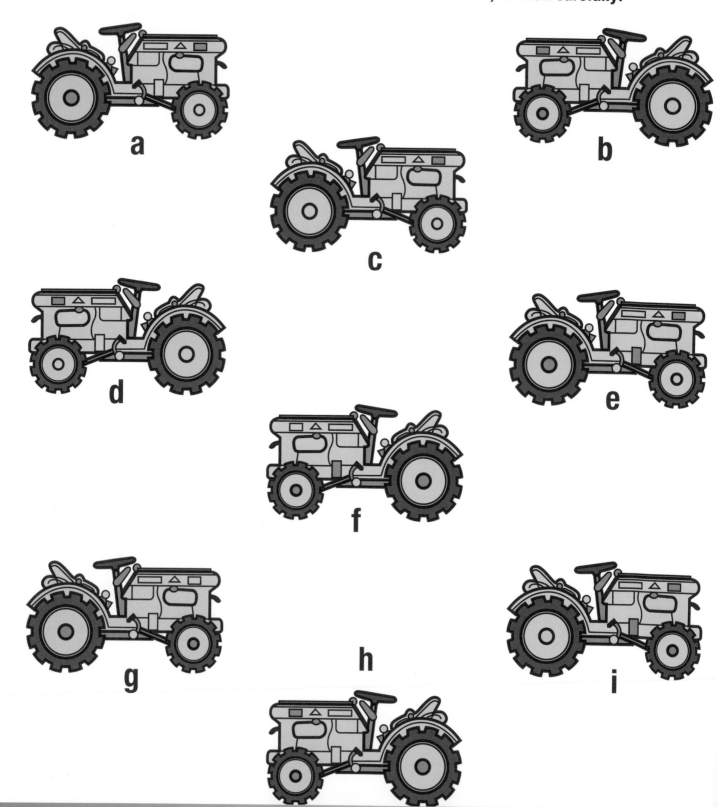

112 DIFFICULTY ✪✪✪✪✪✩✩✩✩✩

⏱ 2 Minutes

Study this picture for two minutes, then see if you can answer the questions on the next page.

113 DIFFICULTY ✪✪✪✪✪✩✩✩✩✩

⏱ 5 Minutes

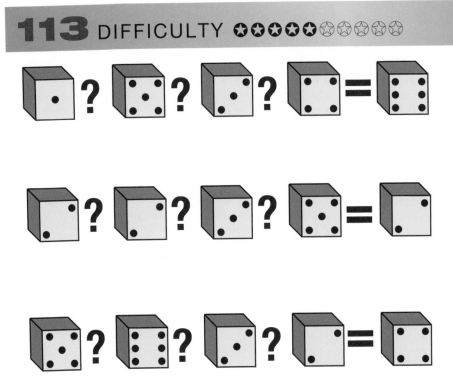

By placing three of the four different mathematical operators (+, -, x, ÷) between the dice in each of the following three calculations, can you arrive at the correct totals, as given?

[112] DIFFICULTY ★★★★★☆☆☆☆☆ ③ Minutes

Can you answer these questions about the puzzle on the previous page without looking back?

1. Which shape is the most abundant?
2. How many circles have red borders and dark blue centers?
3. How many circles have red borders and green centers?
4. How many bordered shapes are there in total?
5. How many shapes have dark blue borders?
6. How many shapes have green borders?
7. How many squares have green borders?
8. What is the total number of red-bordered circles plus red-bordered stars?

114 DIFFICULTY ★★★★★★☆☆☆☆ ⑥ Minutes

All of these butterflies may look identical, but one is different from the rest. Which is the odd one out?

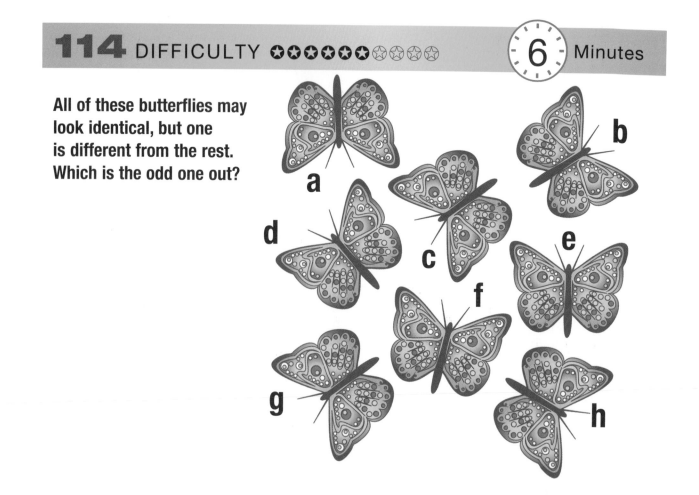

115 DIFFICULTY ✪✪✪✪✪✪☆☆☆☆   ⏱ **8** Minutes

In each of the four buildings below, one type of brick is used more or less frequently than it is in the other three buildings. Can you determine the different brick in each construction? The ten brick types are as follows:

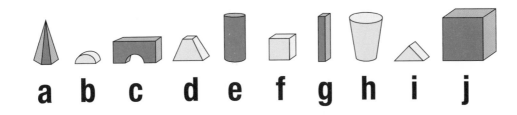

a   b   c   d   e   f   g   h   i   j

Building 2

Building 1

Building 3

Building 4

116 DIFFICULTY ✪✪✪✪✪✪✪✪☆☆   ⑤ Minutes

Which of the four boxed figures (a, b, c, or d) completes the set?

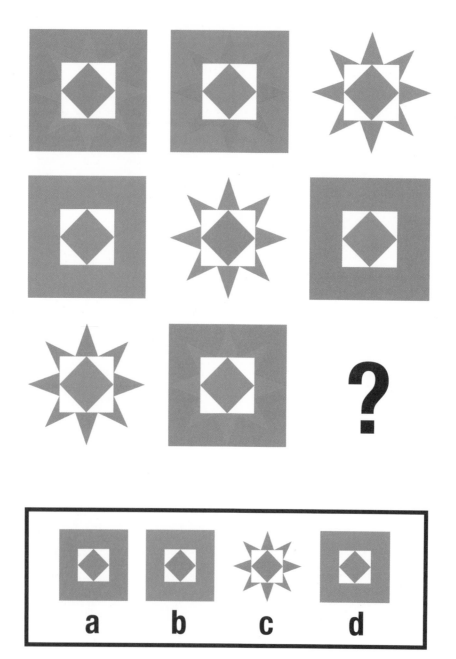

117 DIFFICULTY ★★★★★★★★☆☆

8 Minutes

Can you spot the eleven differences between these two pictures? Circle them in the drawing on the right.

118 DIFFICULTY ★★★★★☆☆☆☆☆

2 Minutes

You have been presented with a tray bearing five bags that should each contain 100 gold coins, except you have been told that one of them contains only 99. You quickly arrange the bags to reveal the one that's short. How?

119 DIFFICULTY ✪✪✪✪✪✪✪✩✩ 6 Minutes

Which three sets of bricks will fit together to form a perfect cube of the same shape as this gray one?

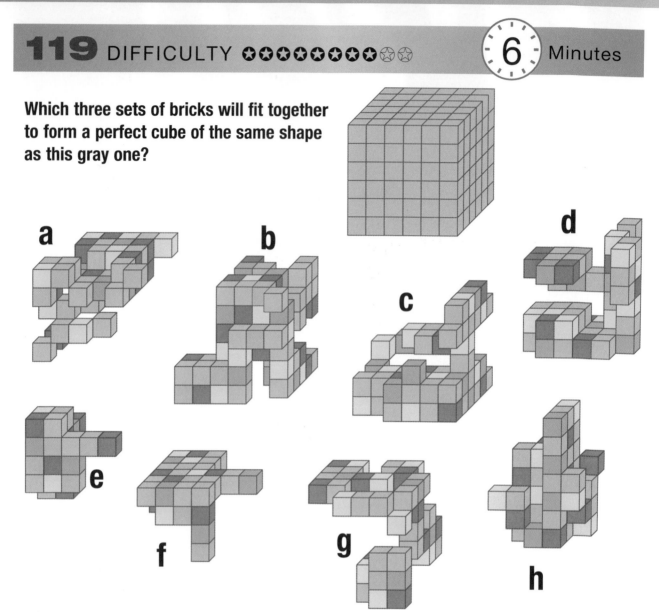

120 DIFFICULTY ✪✪✪✪✪✪✪✪✩✩ 6 Minutes

Can you divide this grid into five sections, each containing five different shapes of five different colors?

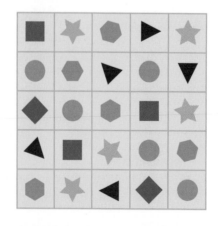

Which of the four boxed figures (a, b, c, or d) completes the set?

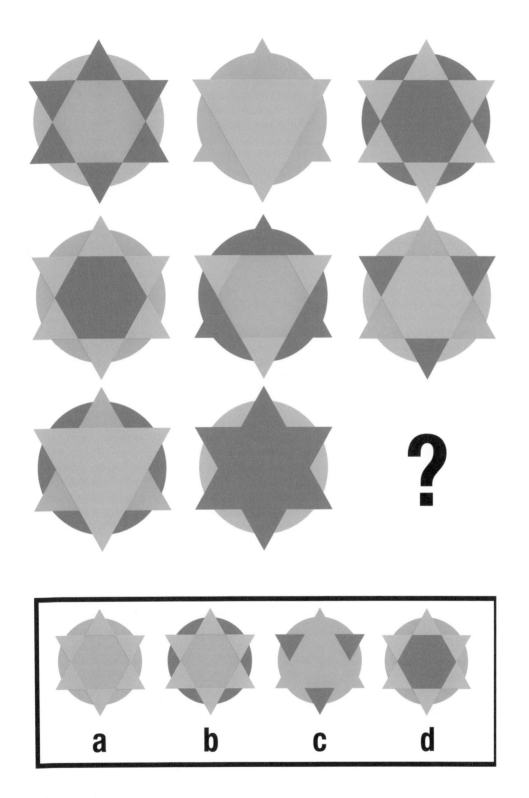

a   b   c   d

122 DIFFICULTY ✪✪✪✪✪✪✪☆☆☆

8 Minutes

Find your way through this fortified maze to the chair in the central chamber.

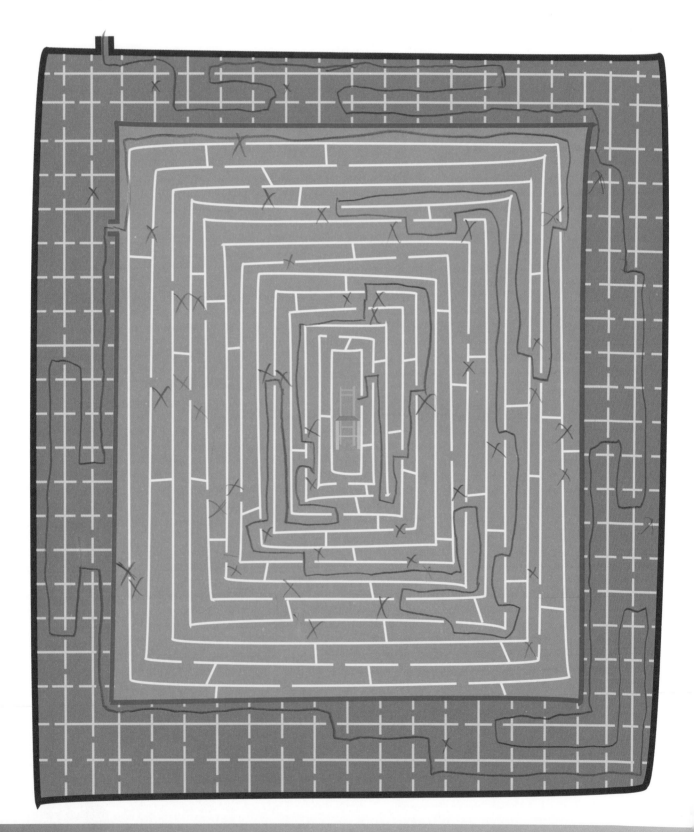

123 DIFFICULTY ✪✪✪✪✪✪✪☆☆☆   ⏱ 5 Minutes

At first glance, these patios may look identical, although they have been photographed from different angles. However, only two are identical. Can you spot them?

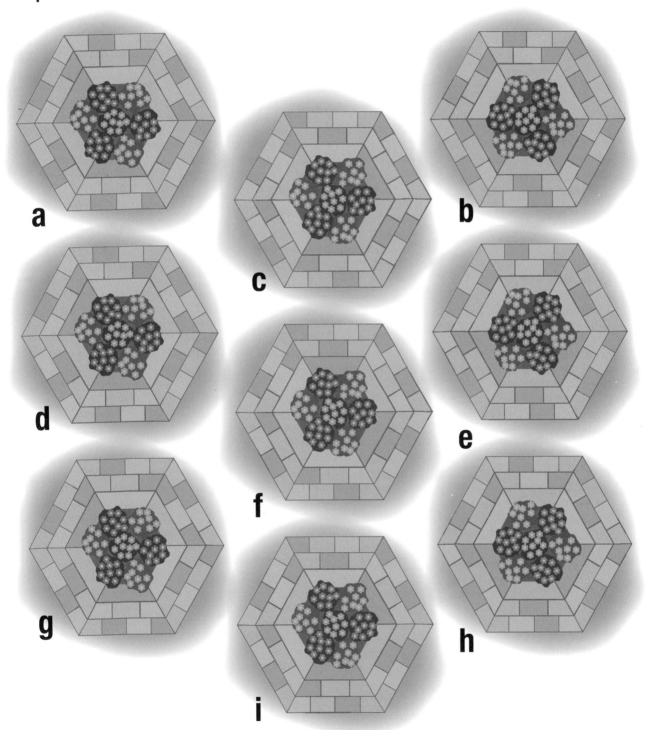

124 DIFFICULTY ✪✪✪✪✪✪✩✩✩✩ ③ Minutes

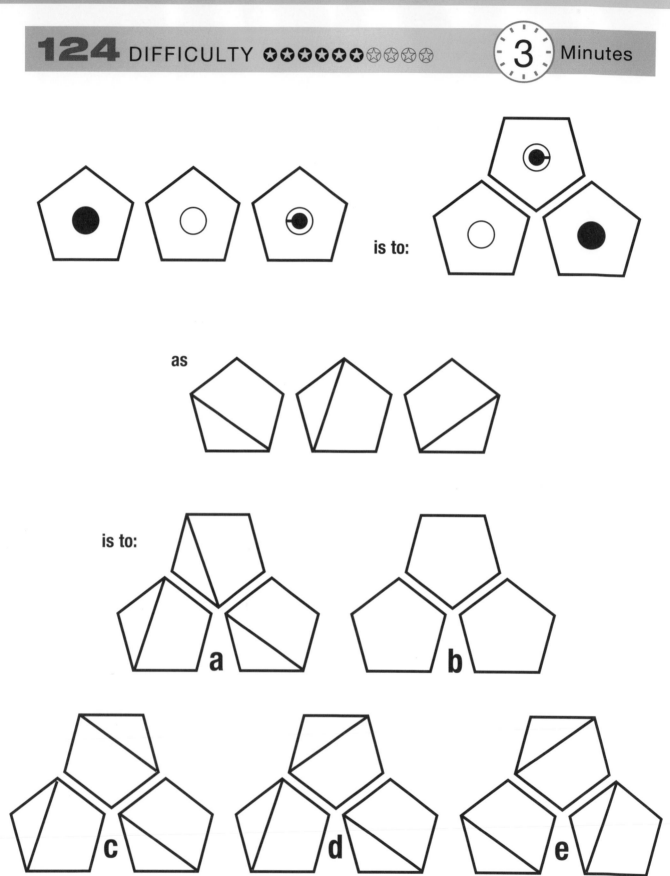

is to:

as

is to:

125 DIFFICULTY ⭐⭐⭐⭐☆☆☆☆☆☆ ② Minutes

To play this wall-building game, you need to draw a set of approximately 25 connected regions. We've done this by drawing overlapping circles, but it really doesn't matter what your "map" looks like.

Two players take turns drawing a wall that connects three unused regions. The first player that cannot make a valid move loses the game.

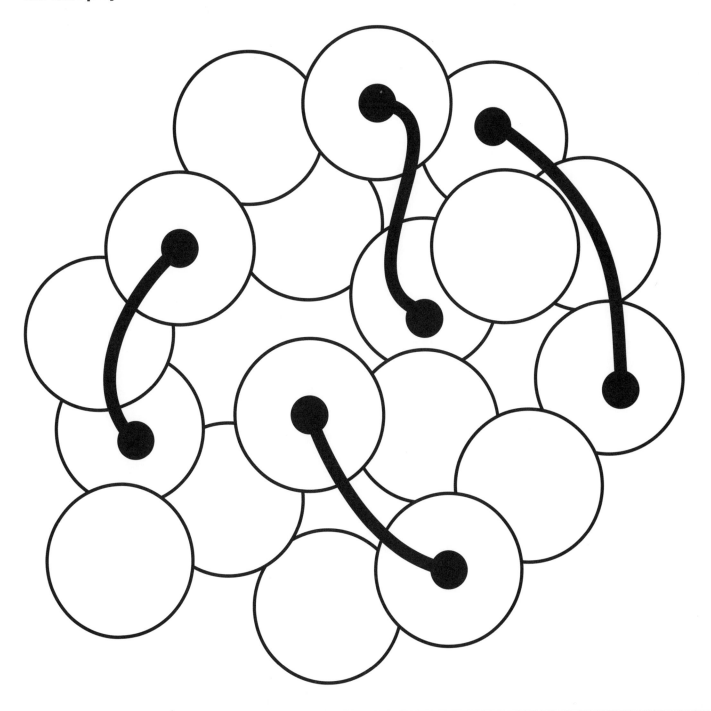

126 DIFFICULTY ✪✪✪✪✪✪✪☆☆ | ⑥ Minutes

Without rotating or reflecting any, can you spot which three hexagons are identical in color?

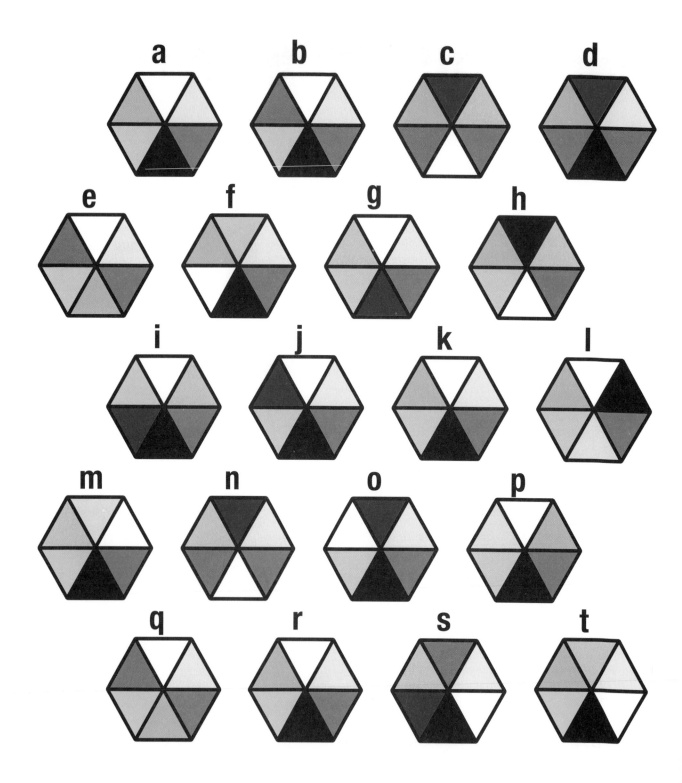

127 DIFFICULTY ✪✪✪✪✪✪✪✰✰✰  5 Minutes

Which of the four boxed figures (a, b, c, or d) completes the set?

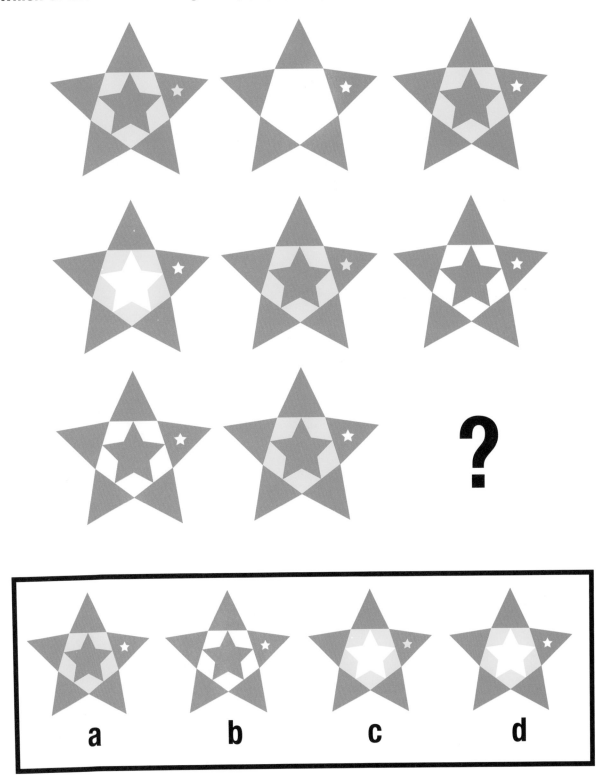

a   b   c   d

1

2

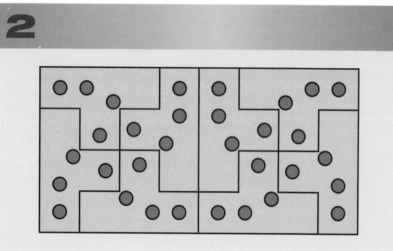

3

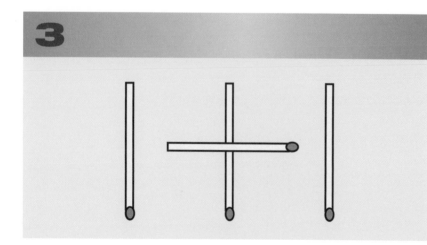

4

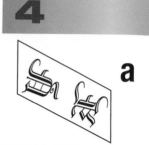

a

5

c; each vertical and horizontal line contains one shape with all green triangles, one with all pink triangles, and one with half pink and half green triangles. Each line also contains two shapes with a red dot in the center and one with no red dot. The missing shape must have all green triangles and a red dot.

6

7

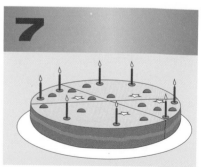

8

Kirsty wins in the fewest moves.

9

a=5, b=7, c=1, d=3, e=2, f=6, and g=4

10

Place stepping stones on the grid rather than making consecutive steps.

11

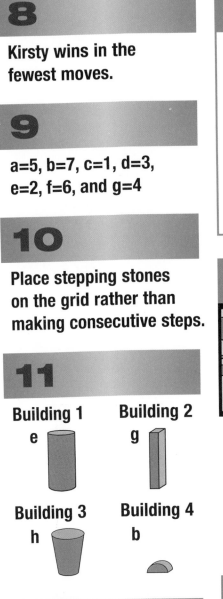

Building 1
e

Building 2
g

Building 3
h

Building 4
b

12

Gary won $8. The total payback is the number of spots on the opposite side of the first die multiplied by the number of spots on the opposite side of the second. Thus Gary got back $20 (5 x 4 = 20), winning $8.

13

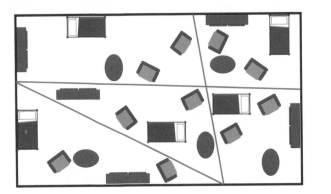

14

If you color in the areas like a political map, you will see that x and y are different colored areas. This means that since x is inside the loop, y is outside the loop.

15

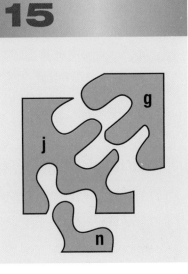

16

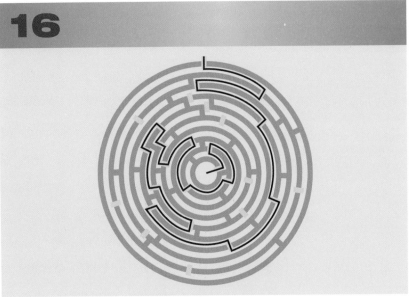

17

18

d; all figures originally outside the hexagon transfer to the inside of the hexagon, and vice versa. Also, black circles turn to white triangles, white circles turn to black triangles, and vice versa.

19

c

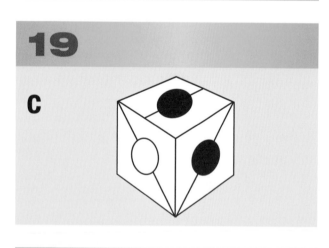

20

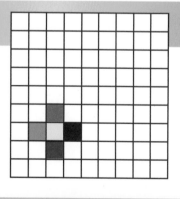

21

22

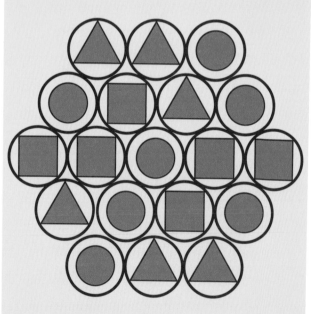

A circle. Every triangle of six circles, must contain different numbers of circles, squares, and triangles.

23

There are ten differences between the two pictures.

24

$([6 + 4] \div 5) - 1 = 1$
$([2 + 6] - 5) \times 1 = 3$
$([4 \times 4] \div 2) - 3 = 5$

25

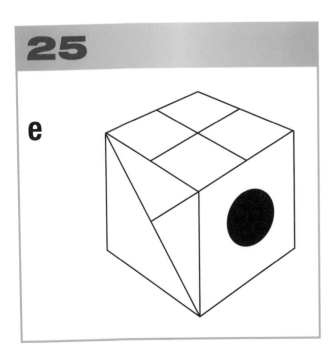

26

1. Blue
2. 3
3. Green
4. 3
5. 2
6. 8
7. 2
8. 25

27

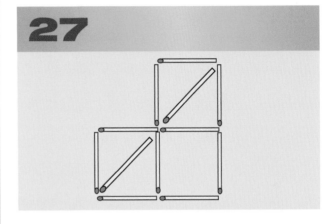

28

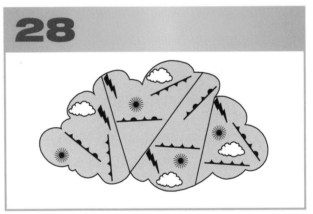

29

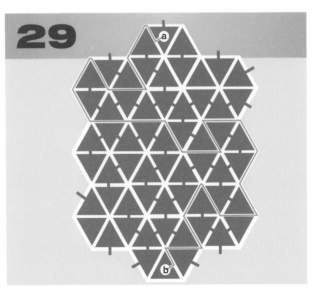

30

A circle. Each row and column, across and down, has thirteen corners.

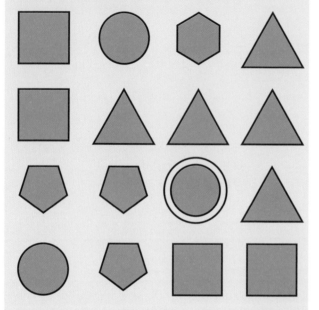

31

a; the circles on the line at the extreme left change places. The line on the extreme right points down instead of up.

32

a; it is looking in a different direction.

33

34

1. 36	5. 3
2. c and f	6. d
3. 11	7. 5
4. b	8. b

35

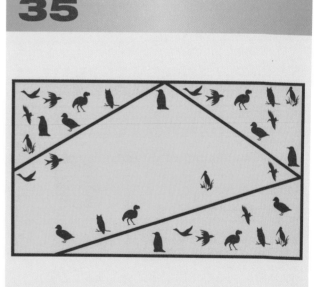

36

None. Rearrange them as follows:

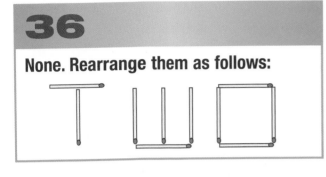

37

48; multiply the number of dots on the top face of each die by the total of the number of dots on the (visible) front and side, then deduct the sum of the dots on the three hidden faces of each die.

38

22; Angelica can see the top faces of all three dice, thus a total of nine spots. The opposite sides of a die have spots that add up to seven. On the left die, the side face Angelica can see has six spots. On the central die, the side face Angelica can see has two spots. On the right die, the side face Angelica can see also has two spots. On the bottom face of the right die there is one spot, so the end face of this die (hidden from you) has either three or four spots. If this end face has four spots, then the total number of spots Angelica can see is twenty-three. But Angelica can see a different number of spots than you—and you can see twenty-three. So the end face Angelica can see has three spots. Thus,

Angelica can see a total of nine spots on the top faces, ten spots on the side faces, and three on the end face for a combined total of twenty-two spots.

39

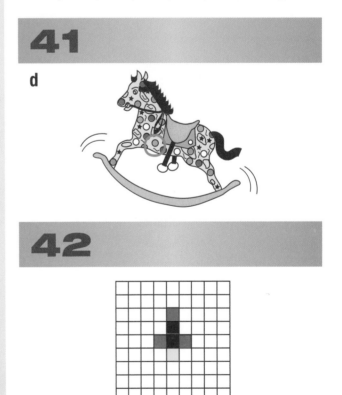

40

a=6, b=7, c=4, d=5, e=2, f=1, and g=3

41

d

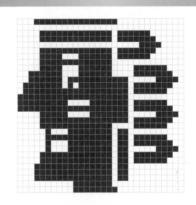

42

43

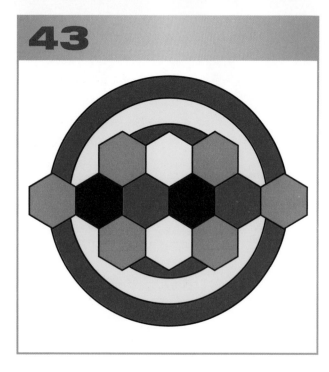

46

47

c and i

44

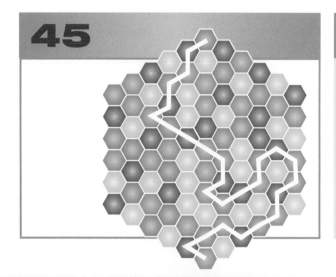

48

Building 1
a
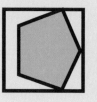

Building 2
c

Building 3
i

Building 4

b

45

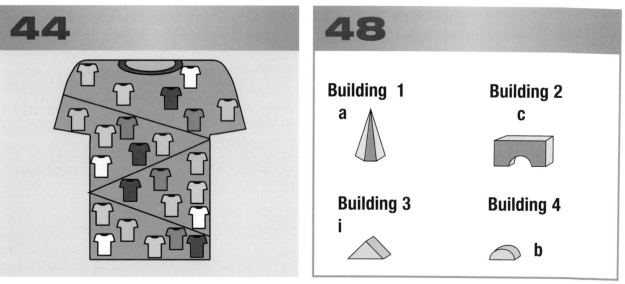

49

a; where shapes touch the side of the square, the shape in the adjacent square must also touch.

50

1. M
2. Yellow
3. Red
4. Red
5. B
6. L
7. Black
8. O

51

Put them on their edges.

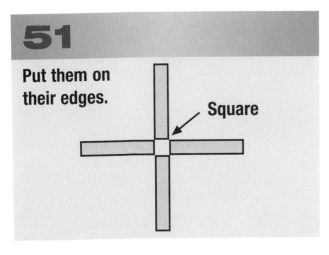

Square

52

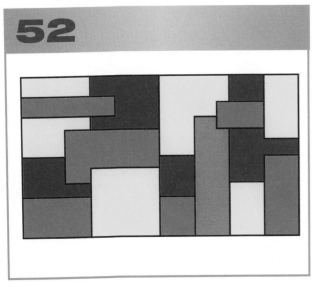

53

Drawing lines inside existing loops will reduce the length of the game but won't guarantee you a win. It's best to plan carefully.

54

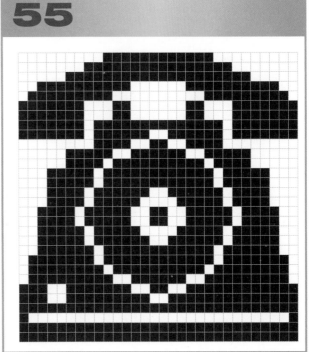

b; the image is the same except that each white arm that points down in the original now points up, and vice versa.

55

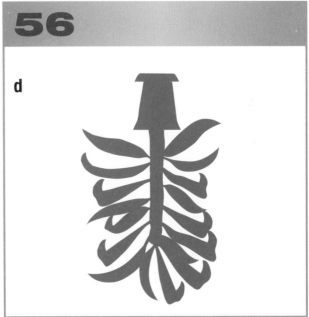

56

d

57

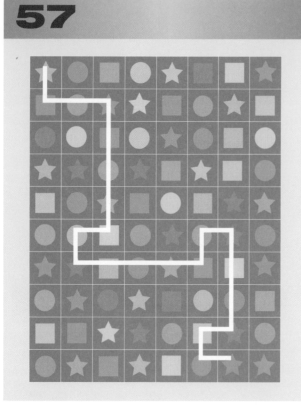

58

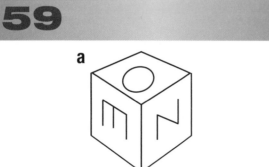

59

a

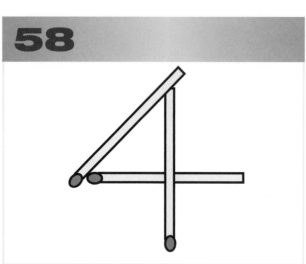

60

f; the points of the central three stars are not aligned.

61

62

f; the figure in the middle rotates 180º and turns from black to white. The three small white squares become one large black square and enclose the figure in the middle.

63

Gary won $4. The total payback is double the difference of the number of spots on the two dice. Thus Gary got back $10: $(6 - 1) \times 2 = 10$, winning $4.

64

1. 5
2. Blue
3. Green
4. White
5. S

6. 3: the T, the S, and the W
7. 2
8. T

65

1=d, 2=f, 3=b, 4=a, 5=c, 6=e

66

There are 21 dots on each die, thus a total of 84 dots on the four dice. Since 34 dots are visible, the total number of dots on the sides that are not visible amounts to 50.

67

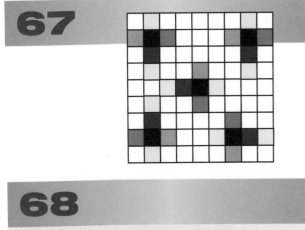

68

Tom wins in the fewest moves.

69

70

g; the bottom two stripes on her shirt are different.

71

72

The minute hand of the clock in the bottom-right corner is incorrect. It should be pointing at the five minutes to the hour position. Now each hour hand points to the minute hand on one of the other clocks so that they lie on the same extended line.

73

a and c

74

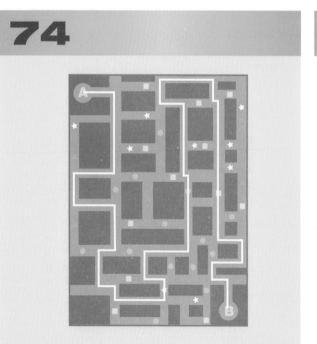

75

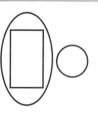

d; the figure in the middle (the rectangle) reduces in size, rotates 90°, and goes inside the figure originally at the bottom (the oval), which increases in size. The figure at the top (the circle) attaches itself to the right-hand side of the oval.

76

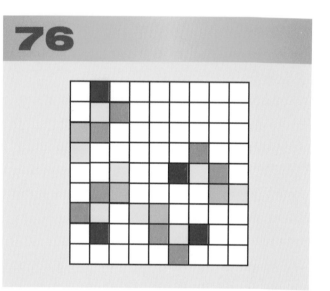

77

78

c and f

79

80

The triangle can be seen to consist of four isosceles triangles, each side being one match in length. The hexagon consists of six of the same-sized triangles, which is twice as big in area.

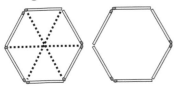

81

c; on each row and column, each shape and each color appears three times.

82

c, h, and k

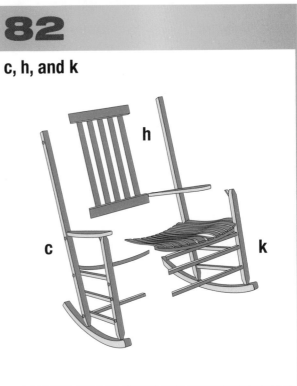

83

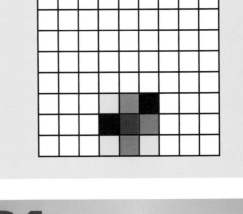

84

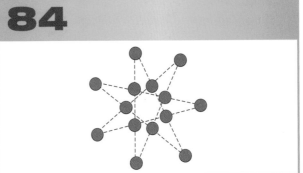

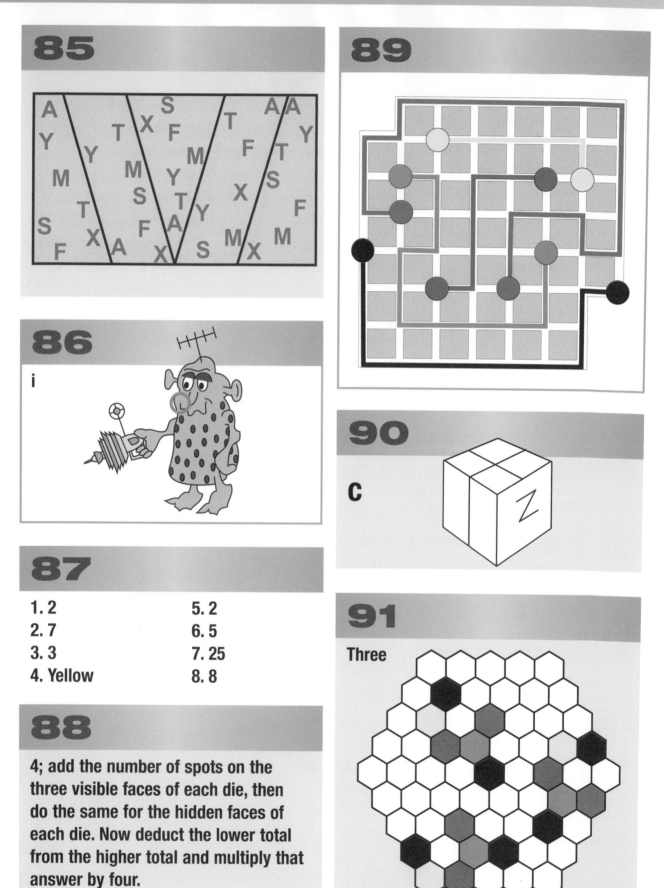

85

86

i

87

1. 2
2. 7
3. 3
4. Yellow
5. 2
6. 5
7. 25
8. 8

88

4; add the number of spots on the three visible faces of each die, then do the same for the hidden faces of each die. Now deduct the lower total from the higher total and multiply that answer by four.

89

90

c

91

Three

92

f

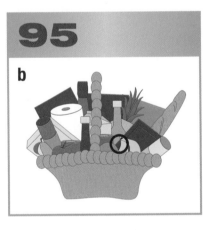

93

1. 9
2. 4
3. d, f, and h
4. 2
5. 1
6. 2
7. c
8. a and i

94

2	6	4	3	5	1
1	3	5	6	4	2
5	4	2	1	6	3
6	1	3	4	2	5
3	5	6	2	1	4
4	2	1	5	3	6

In the diagonal top left to bottom right, there is no 5, so in column 1, the 5 is in row 3, and in row 2, the 5 is in column 3. Thus in row 1, 5 is in column 5, and in column 2, the 5 is in row 5. By elimination, in row 2, the 6 is in column 4, so 6 is also in row 3/column 5, column 1/row 4, and column 3/row 5. Column 5 has 2 in row 4 and 3 in row 6. The number of spots in row 4/column 4 is (by elimination) either 1 or 4 and for a total of 18 spots, if 1 is in row 4/column 4, there would need to be either 6 + 2 or 4 + 4 in the top two squares of that diagonal line. There is a 6 in row 1/column 2, so neither of the top two squares in the diagonal can contain a 6, and since there is 4 in row 2/column 5, there can't be 4 in row 2/column 2. Thus (above) in the diagonal running top left to bottom right, there isn't a 1 in row 4/column 4. Thus row 4/column 4 has 4 and (for a total of 18), the top two squares in that diagonal have 2 and/or 3. The 3 isn't in column 1 (there is already a 3 in that column), so column 1/row 1 is 2 and column 2/row 2 is 3. By elimination, column 1/row 6 is 4, so row 6/column 3 is 1, and row 6/column 2 is 2. Thus (by elimination), column 2/row 4 is 1, column 2/row 3 is 4, row 1/column 3 is 4, row 5/column 4 is 2, row 5/column 6 is 4, and row 2/column 6 is 2. In the diagonal top right to bottom left, spots total 18, so row 1/column 6 is 1 and row 3/column 4 is 1. Thus row 1/column 4 is 3 and row 3/column 6 is 3.

95

b

96

e; the large arc rotates 90° clockwise, and the other two arcs rotate 180°.

97

98

99

b = 4   f = 5
c = 6   g = 3
d = 1

100

101

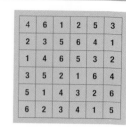

In the diagonal top right to bottom left there is a 4, so in column 3/row 4 there is (by elimination) a 2. In the diagonal top left to bottom right, 4 is in row 1, and column 6/row 6 contains 5. In row 4, 4 is in column 6. In the diagonal top right to bottom left, 5 is in row 3, and column 2/row 5 contains 4. There are six 4s, so the remaining 4 is in column 3/row 5. In row 5, 5 is in column 1; so in row 2, 5 is in column 3, thus 5 is in column 5/row 1, thus row 1 has 1 in column 3. Since there is now 2 in the diagonal top right to bottom left, there isn't 2 in column 1/row 6; so in column 1, 2 is in row 2. Thus in the diagonal top left to bottom right, 3 is in column 2/row 2, and 2 is in column 5/row 5. Remaining 2s are in column 4/row 1 and column 2/row 6. By elimination, row 1 has 6 in column 2 and 3 in column 6. In the top

right/bottom left diagonal, 6 is in row 6, so 1 is in row 5. In column 1, 1 is in row 3 and 3 is in row 4. In row 3, 3 is in column 5. In column 5, 6 is in row 4 and 1 is in row 6. In column 6, 6 is in row 5 and 1 is in row 2, so row 2 has 6 in column 4 and column 4 has 3 in row 5.

102

103

d

104

Don't spread yourself too thinly.
One good network will beat several
smaller ones.

105

b: each vertical and horizontal
line contains one shape the
right way up, one rotated
through 90°, and one rotated
through 180°. Each line also contains
one red shape with a blue outline and
two blue shapes with a red outline. The
missing shape should be the right way
up and blue with a red outline.

106

c and g

107

a = 4
b = 3
c = 5
d = 1

e = 7
f = 6
g = 2

108

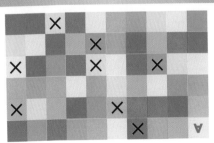

109

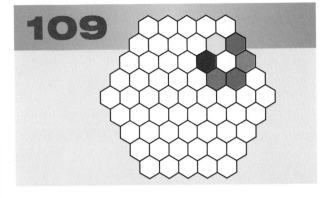

110

An easy way to win is to create a line
of three in the middle of the grid. Your
opponent can't cover both ends at once.

111

c and d

112

1. The star
2. 1
3. 2
4. 14

5. 2
6. 3
7. None
8. 4

113

(1 x 5) − 3 + 4 = 6
(2 x 2) + 3 − 5 = 2
(5 + 6 − 3) ÷ 2 = 4

114

e

115

Building 1	Building 2	Building 3	Building 4

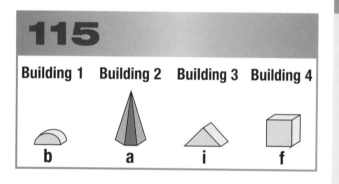

| b | a | i | f |

116

b: each vertical and horizontal line contains one blue, one turquoise, and one white outer box. Each line also contains one blue inner diamond and two turquoise ones. Finally, each line contains one blue star and two turquoise ones. The missing image should be a green outer box with a purple inner diamond and a green star.

117

118

Balance the tray on one bag, then place the other four bags as shown. The bag on the part of the tray that rises is light. If it stays level, then the bag underneath is the light one, which contains 99 coins.

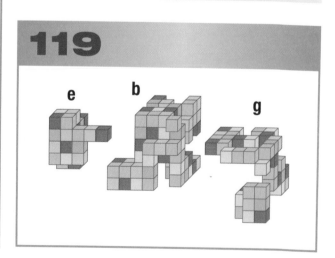

119

e   b   g

120

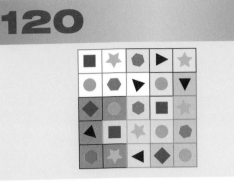

121

a; each vertical and horizontal line contains one light green, one dark green, and one orange circle. Each line also contains one light green, one dark green, and one orange hexagon. Each line contains right-side-up triangles in light green, dark green, and orange. Finally, each line contains two inverted triangles in light green and one in dark green. The missing image should be of an orange circle with an orange hexagon and both triangles in light green.

122

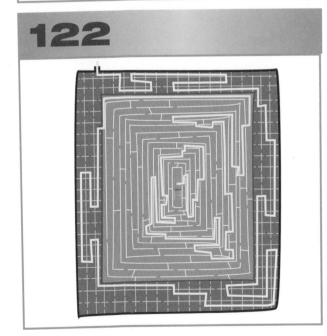

123

c and h

124

d; the pentagon on the left goes to the bottom right, the pentagon on the right goes to the top, having rotated 180°, and the pentagon in the middle goes to the bottom left.

125

The first few moves don't matter. The skill lies in planning your end game.

126

a, k, and r

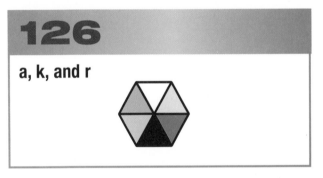

127

c; each vertical and horizontal line contains one white pentagon and two yellow ones, one white inner star and two red ones, and one small yellow star and two small white ones. The missing shape should have a yellow pentagon, a white inner star, and a small yellow star.

ACKNOWLEDGMENTS ✪ SPATIAL PUZZLES

✪ Puzzle contributors

Contributors are listed next to the numbers of the puzzles they created.

✪ Brainwarp

Puzzles 3, 22, 27, 30, 36, 49, 51, 58, 80, 81, 84, 118

✪ David Bodycombe

Puzzles 6, 10, 14, 20, 42, 43, 52, 53, 67, 71, 72, 76, 83, 89, 90, 104, 109, 110, 125

✪ Guy Campbell

Puzzles 1, 5, 16, 21, 29, 39, 45, 55, 57, 74, 77, 97, 105, 121, 122, 127

✪ Philip Carter

Puzzles 18, 19, 25, 31, 54, 59, 62, 75, 91, 96, 103, 124

✪ Puzzler Media Ltd

Puzzles 2, 4, 7, 8, 9, 11, 12, 13, 15, 17, 23, 24, 26, 28, 32, 33, 34, 35, 37, 38, 40, 41, 44, 46, 47, 48, 50, 56, 60, 61, 63, 64, 65, 66, 68, 69, 70, 73, 78, 79, 82, 85, 86, 87, 88, 92, 93, 94, 95, 98, 99, 100, 101, 102, 106, 107, 108, 111, 112, 113, 114, 115, 116, 117, 119, 120, 123, 126

Spatial Puzzles was commissioned, edited, designed, and produced by:
Book Creation Ltd., 20 Lochaline Street, London W6 9SH, United Kingdom
Managing Director: Hal Robinson
Editor: David Popey **Art Editor:** Keith Miller
Designer: Justin Hunt **Copy Editor:** Sarah Barlow **Editorial Assistant:** Claire Bratt

Bonus Puzzles

1 DIFFICULTY ✪✪✪✪✪✪☆☆☆☆

(3) Minutes

Follow the arrows in the grid below to get to the yellow star.

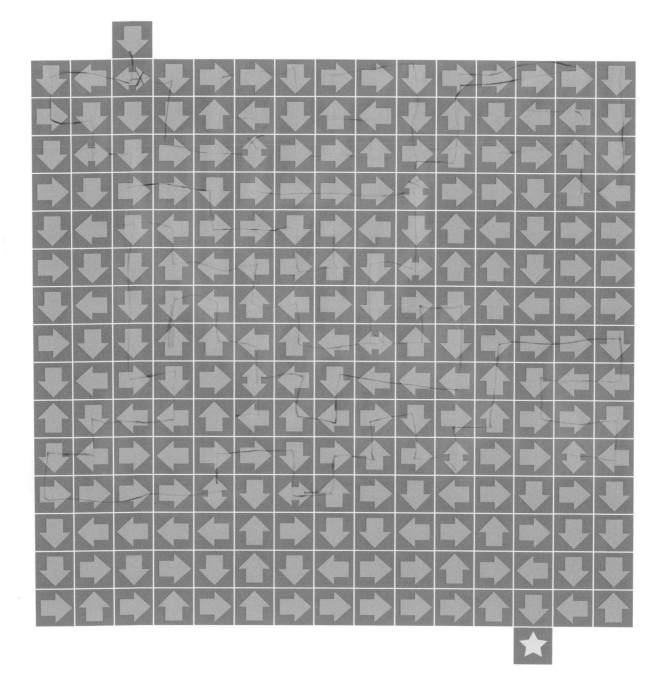

Which of the figures below (a, b, or c) completes the grid?

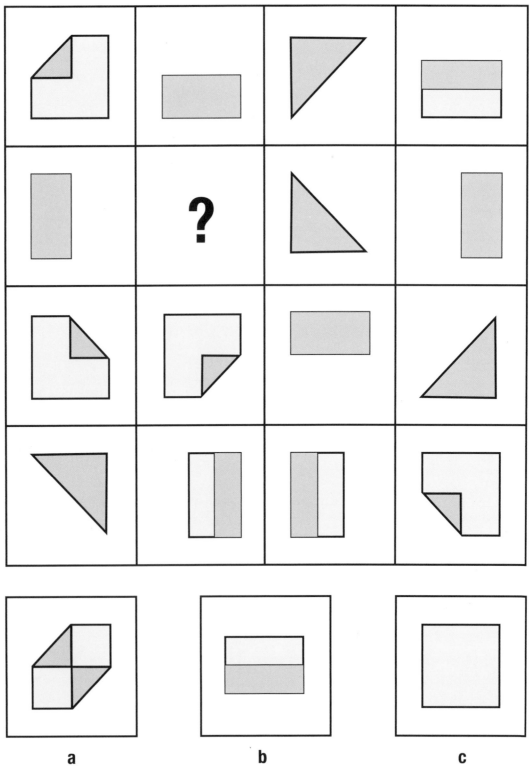

a   b   c

3 DIFFICULTY ✪✪✪✪✪✪☆☆☆☆ | ⏱ **2** Minutes

Study this picture for two minutes, then see if you can answer the questions on page 262.

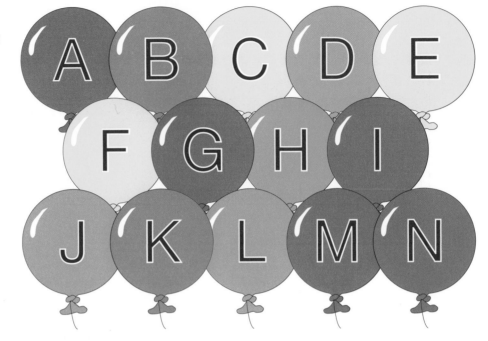

4 DIFFICULTY ✪✪✪✪✪✪✪☆☆☆ | ⏱ **4** Minutes

Here are ten matches. How can you take one away but still be left with ten?

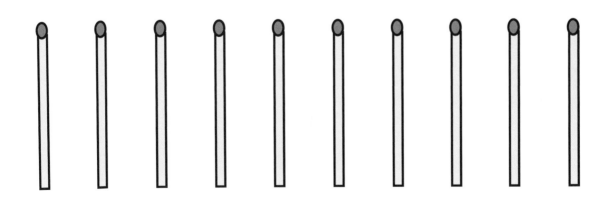

Can you answer these questions about the puzzle on page 261 without looking back?

1. Which letter appears on the green balloon?

2. How many balloons are orange?

3. What is the color of balloon G?

4. What letter appears on the balloon touching both balloon L and balloon M?

5. What is the color of balloon B?

6. What is the color of the balloon below and to the left of balloon F?

7. Which balloon color appears most often in the picture?

8. How many balloons are in the picture?

Using four straight lines only, can you divide this tree into six sections, each containing the leaves of five different trees?

In each of the four buildings below, one type of brick is used less frequently than it is in the other three buildings. Can you discover the different brick in each construction? The ten brick types are as follows:

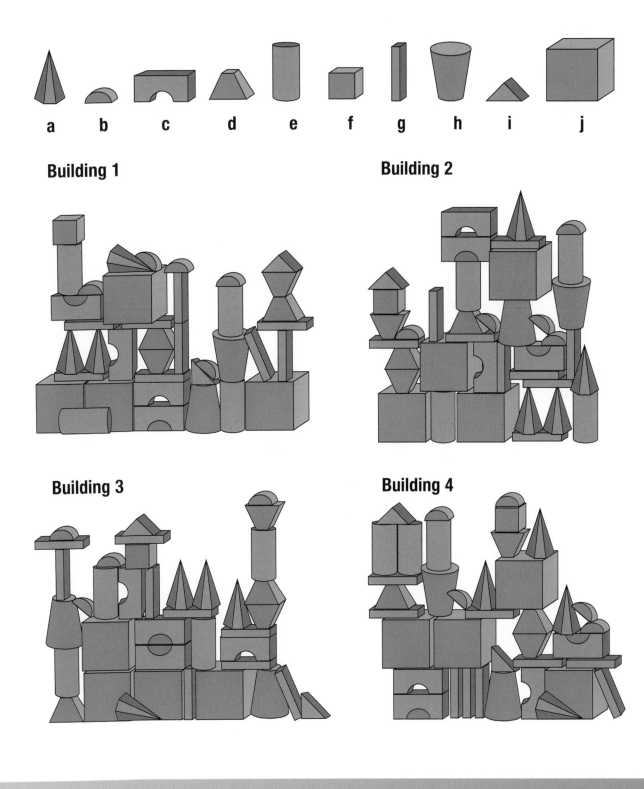

a   b   c   d   e   f   g   h   i   j

Building 1

Building 2

Building 3

Building 4

7 DIFFICULTY ✪✪✪✪✪☆✪☆✪☆✪   ⏱ **3** Minutes

Which of the four boxed figures (a, b, c, or d) completes the set?

a   b   c   d

8 DIFFICULTY ✪✪✪✪✩✩✩✩✩✩    **2** Minute

Rosemary's magic mirror reflects very strangely! Can you match each duck to its correct (although misplaced and somewhat distorted) image in the mirror?

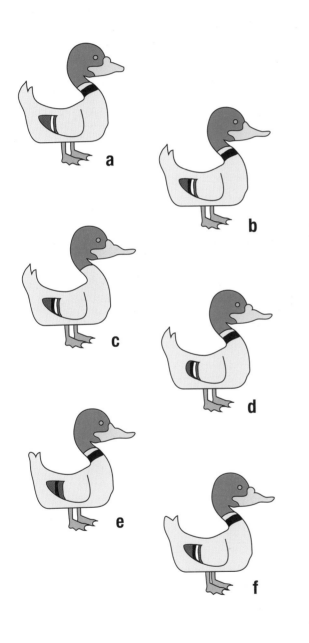

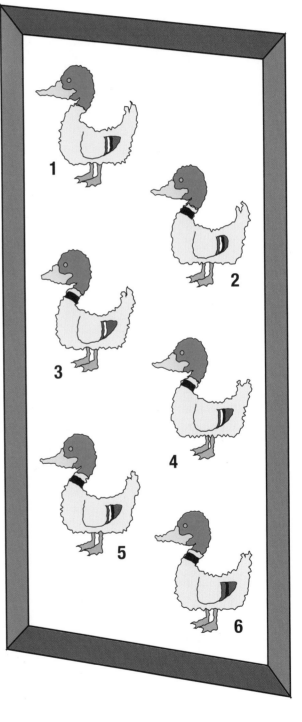

9 DIFFICULTY ★★★★☆☆☆☆☆☆ ⏱ **5** Minutes

Given that scales a and b balance perfectly, how many triangles are needed to balance scale c?

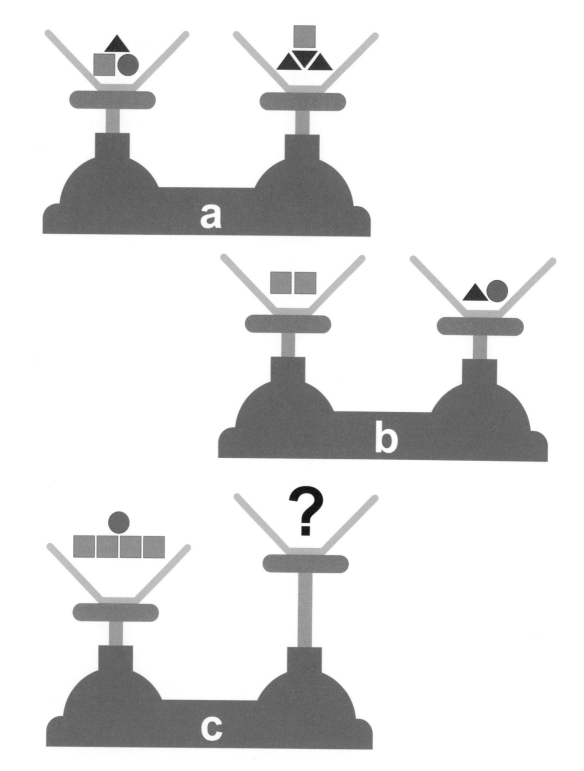

10 DIFFICULTY ✪✪✪✪✪✪☆☆☆☆   (10) Minutes

Kirsty played a game of Snakes and Ladders with her brother Tom. He threw the first 6, so started first, placing his playing piece on the 6. After that, every time it was Kirsty's turn, her die followed the sequence 4, 2, 6, 3, 5, 1; so her first move was to square 4, then square 6, etc. After his first turn when he threw the 6, Tom's die followed the sequence 1, 5, 4, 3, 2, 6 each time, so his second move was to square 7, his third was to square 12, etc. The normal rules of the game were followed, so whenever someone landed on a square that had the foot of a ladder, the piece was moved to the top of the ladder. Whenever someone landed on a square that had the head of a snake, the piece was moved to the tail of the snake. The number thrown to end the game didn't necessarily matter, since the first person to move a piece completely off the board won. Who won the game—Kirsty or Tom?

100	99	98	97	96	95	94	93	92	91
81	82	83	84	85	86	87	88	89	90
80	79	78	77	76	75	74	73	72	71
61	62	63	64	65	66	67	68	69	70
60	59	58	57	56	55	54	53	52	51
41	42	43	44	45	46	47	48	49	50
40	39	38	37	36	35	34	33	32	31
21	22	23	24	25	26	27	28	29	30
20	19	18	17	16	15	14	13	12	11
1	2	3	4	5	6	7	8	9	10

START →

11 DIFFICULTY ✪✪✪✪✰✰✰✰✰

3 Minutes

By touching one coin only, make two rows of three heads. You may not turn any coins over.

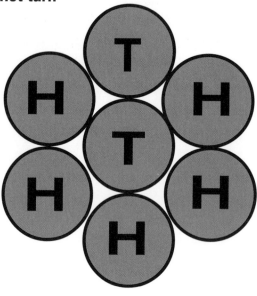

12 DIFFICULTY ✪✪✪✪✰✰✰✰✰✰

3 Minutes

Which three differently colored pieces can be fitted together to form a copy of this star? Pieces may be rotated, but not flipped over.

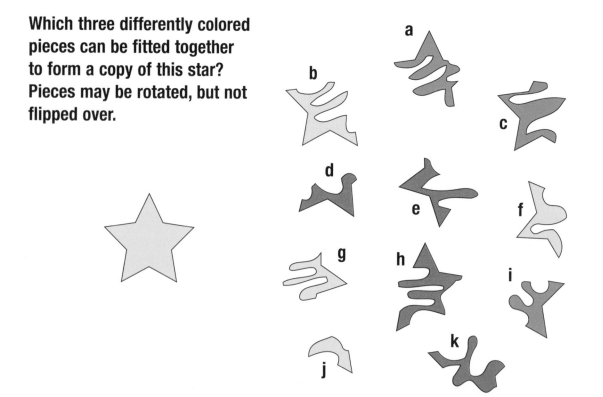

13 DIFFICULTY ★★★★★★☆☆☆☆ 4 Minutes

Place the cards on the left into the colored grid so that each horizontal row and vertical column contains an ace, two, three, four, and five of hearts; and each shape (shown by the different colors) also contains an ace, two, three, four, and five of hearts. Some cards are already in their correct positions.

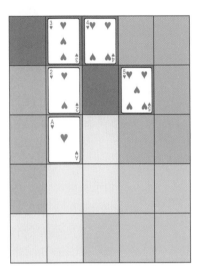

14 DIFFICULTY ★★★★★★☆☆☆☆ 4 Minutes

By drawing three straight lines, can you divide this circle into five sections, each containing two green stars, one red star, one yellow star, one blue star, and one black star?

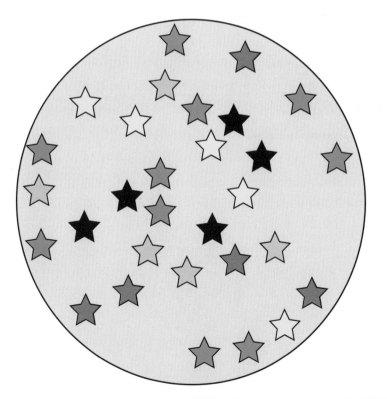

15 DIFFICULTY ★★★★☆☆☆☆☆☆   ③ Minutes

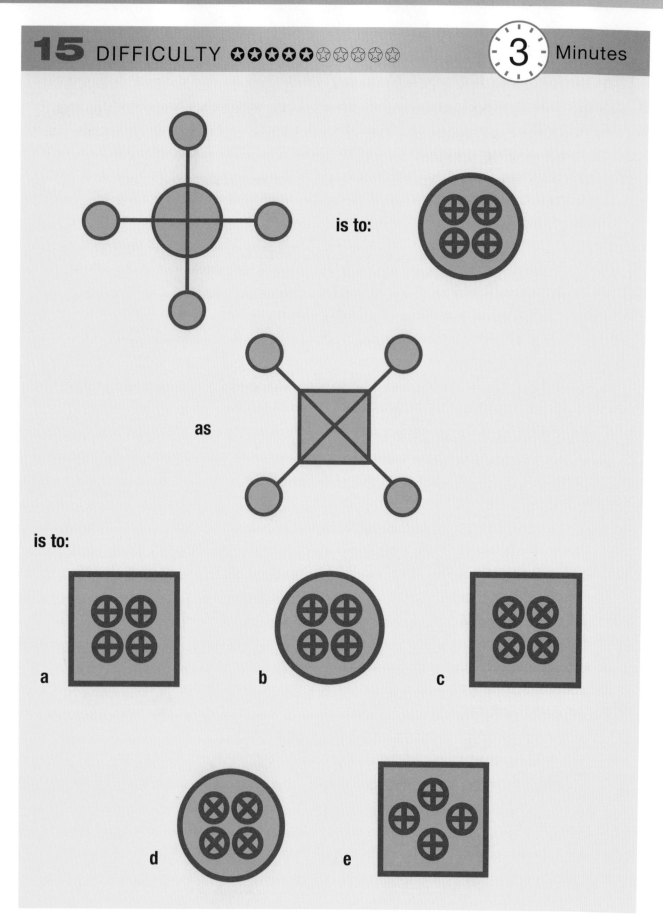

is to:

as

is to:

a

b

c

d

e

16 DIFFICULTY ✪✪✪✪✪✪☆☆☆☆☆ 4 Minutes

This grid of dominoes should have the same total of spots in each row and column, but two pieces have been moved out of position. Can you put them back in the right place?

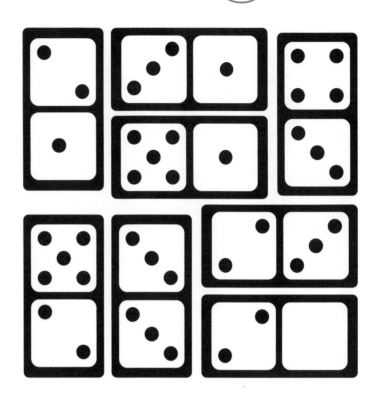

17 DIFFICULTY ✪✪✪✪✪☆☆☆☆☆ 4 Minutes

Can you pair up these door keys with the imprints of their ends?

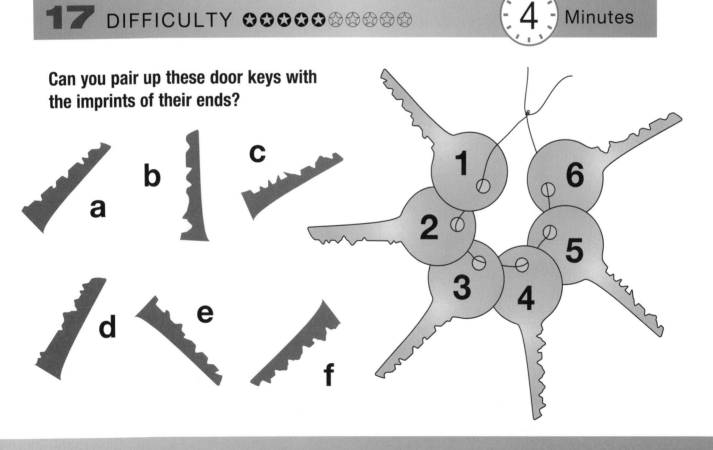

18 DIFFICULTY ★★★★★★★☆☆☆

30 Minutes

Don't let this numbergram put you out to pasture.

HOW TO DO A NUMBERGRAM:

Along each row or column, there are numbers that indicate how many blocks of black squares are in a line. For example, "3, 4, 5" indicates that from left to right or top to bottom, there is a group of three black squares, then a group of four black squares, then another group of five black squares.

Each block of black squares on the same line must have at least one white square between it and the next block of black squares. Blocks of black squares may or may not have a number of white squares before and after them.

It is sometimes possible to determine which squares will be black without reference to other lines or columns. It is helpful to put a small dot in a square you know will be empty.

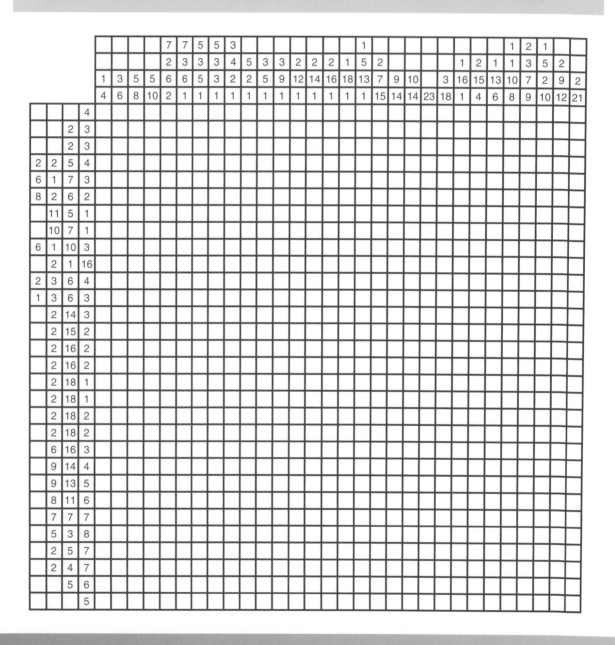

19 DIFFICULTY ✪✪✪✪✩✩✩✩✩✩ ④ Minutes

Using three straight lines, can you divide this star into six sections, each containing six different shapes?

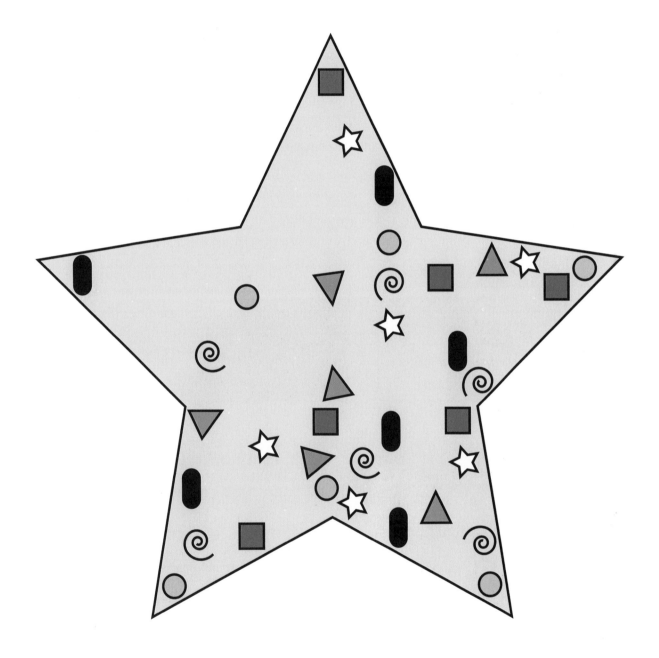

20 DIFFICULTY ✪✪✪✪✪☆☆☆☆☆ ⏱ 5 Minutes

Using yellow, red, blue, and green only, can you color this map so that no two touching areas have the same color?

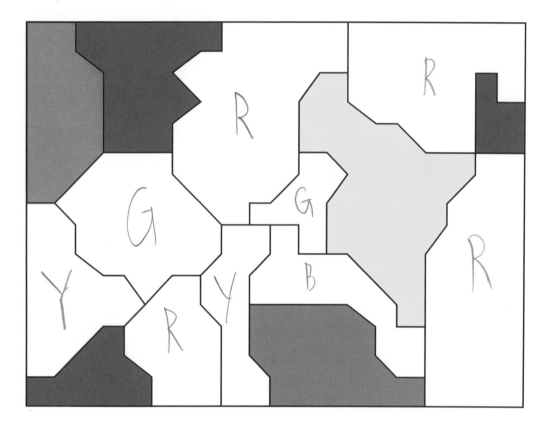

21 DIFFICULTY ✪✪✪✪✪✪☆☆☆☆ ⏱ 4 Minutes

What should the hour hand point to on clock d in this sequence?

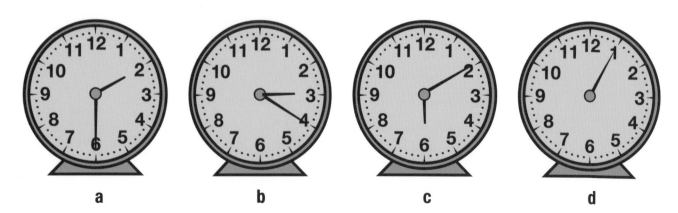

a   b   c   d

22 DIFFICULTY ✪✪✪✪✪✪☆☆☆☆   ⏱ **5** Minutes

Which of the four squares (a, b, c, or d) should go in the center of the grid?

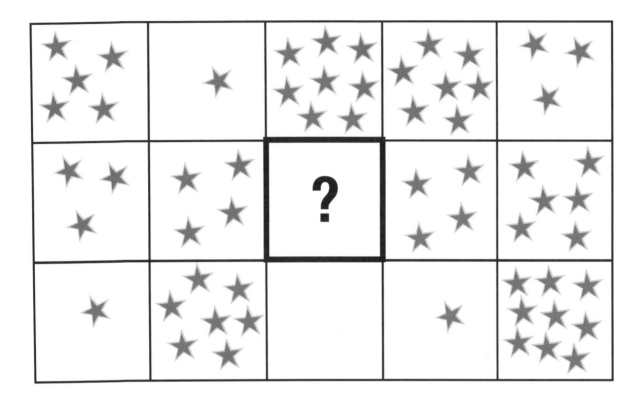

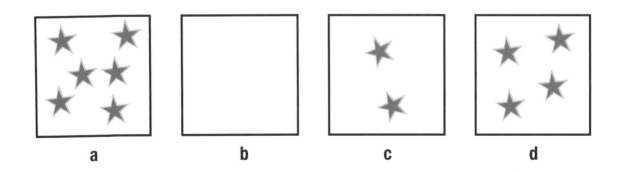

a   b   c   d

23 DIFFICULTY ✪✪✪✪✪☆☆☆☆☆ ⏱ 5 Minutes

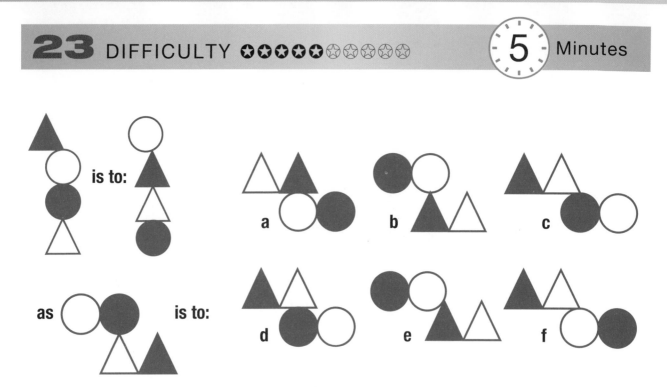

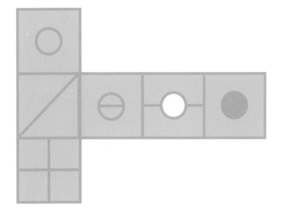

24 DIFFICULTY ✪✪✪✪✪✪☆☆☆☆ ⏱ 3 Minutes

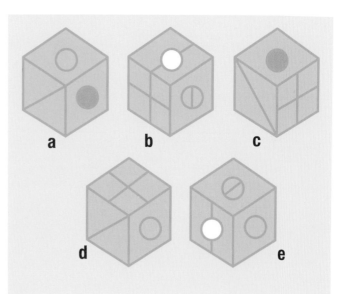

When the above is folded to form a cube, which one of the options opposite (a, b, c, d, or e) is produced?

25 DIFFICULTY ✪✪✪✪✪✪☆☆☆☆ ⏱ **5** Minutes

Which of the four boxed figures (a, b, c, or d) completes the set?

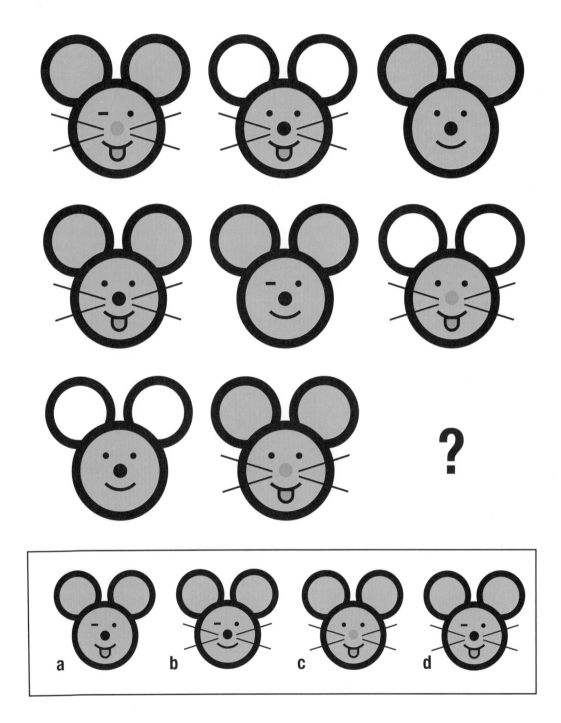

In the game of solitaire, the aim is to jump one blue disk over another (horizontally or vertically), removing the disk you jumped over from the board until only one piece remains. Jumps can occur only over one disk, and you must land on an empty space. The aim is to end up with just one blue disk remaining.

On this unusual board, a few of the squares have been left blank. You must remain within the area marked out by the game board at all times. There may be more than one solution. You could use a piece of squared paper and some coins to play this game.

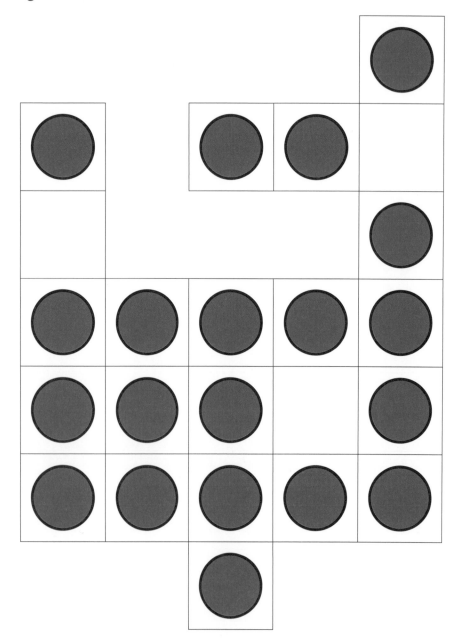

27 DIFFICULTY ✪✪✪✪☆☆☆☆☆☆

4 Minutes

At 4:00 p.m. on February 26, 2000, Jason started his course work. He expected it to take him 86 minutes, but he finished a quarter-hour early. So he left immediately for a vacation and returned exactly a week later. What time and date was it on Jason's digital 24-hour watch when he returned?

28 DIFFICULTY ✪✪✪✪✪☆☆☆☆☆

4 Minutes

By drawing three straight lines, can you divide this polygon into five sections, each containing seven different shapes?

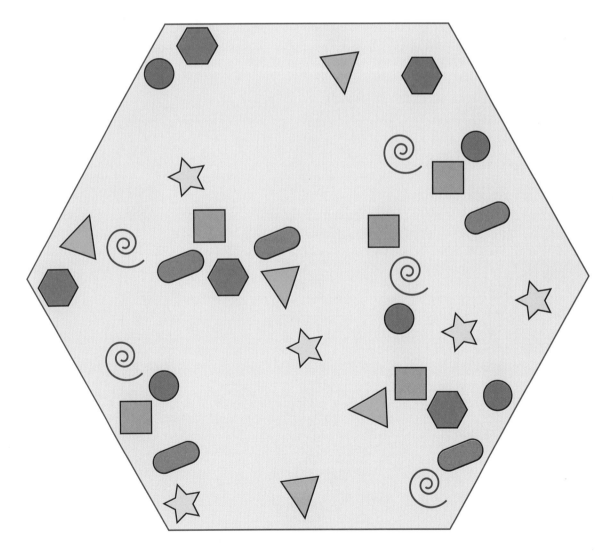

29 DIFFICULTY ✪✪✪✪✪✪✪☆☆☆   ⏱ **5** Minutes

There are two identical pairs among these nine bottles. Can you spot them?

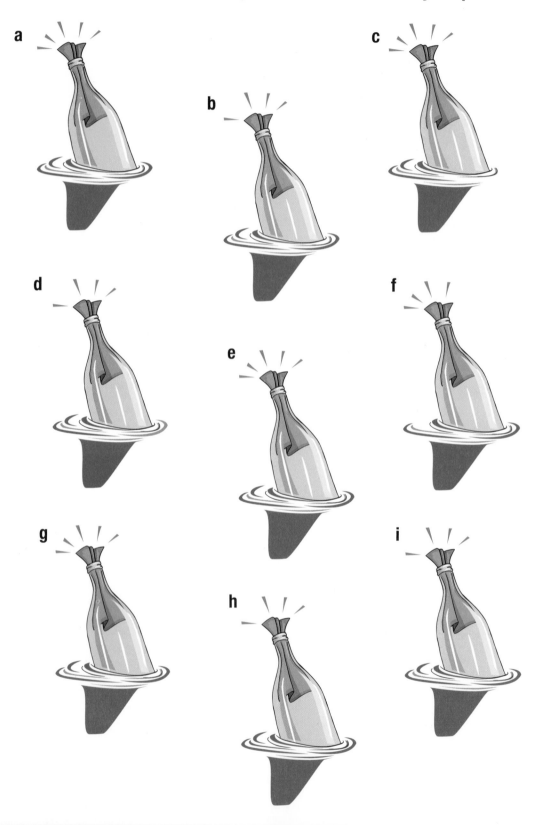

30 DIFFICULTY ✪✪✪✪✪☆☆☆☆☆ ⑥ Minutes

Only two of these patterns are the same. Can you spot the identical pair?

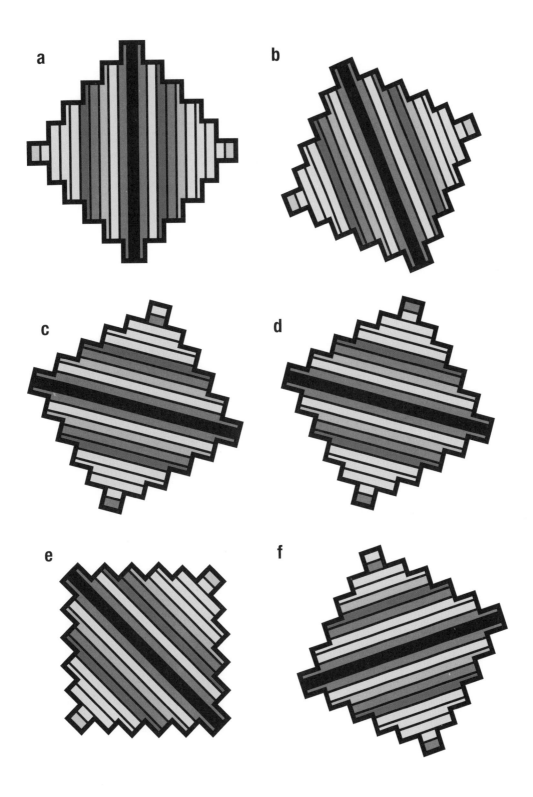

a b c d e f

31 DIFFICULTY ✪✪✪✪✪✪✩✩✩✩   5 Minutes

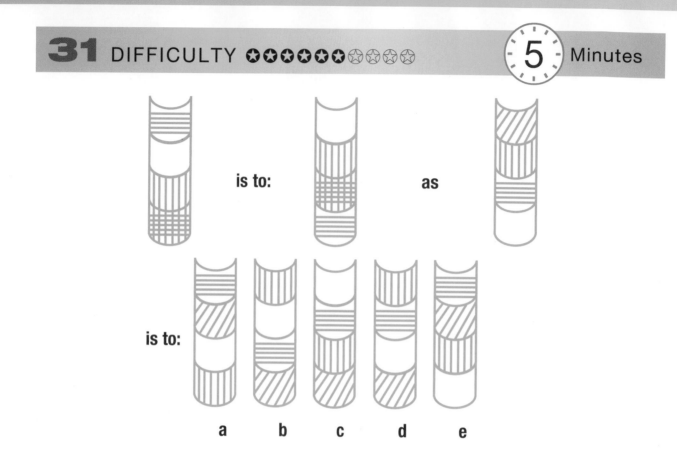

is to: as

is to:

a   b   c   d   e

32 DIFFICULTY ✪✪✪✪✪✪✩✩✩✩   4 Minutes

Which two of these squares are the same shade as the one at the bottom right?

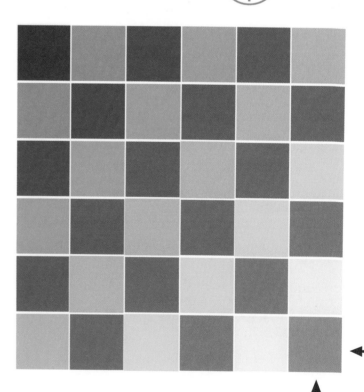

33 DIFFICULTY ✪✪✪✪✪✪✪✩✩

6 Minutes

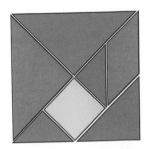

Can you fit the two sets of colored shapes into the shaded areas in this tangram puzzle? Pieces may be rotated, but not flipped over, and no piece may overlap another. (Hint: each figure is made up of one set of pieces.)

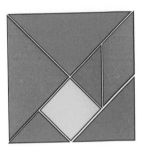

34 DIFFICULTY ✪✪✪✪✪✪✩✩✩✩

4 Minutes

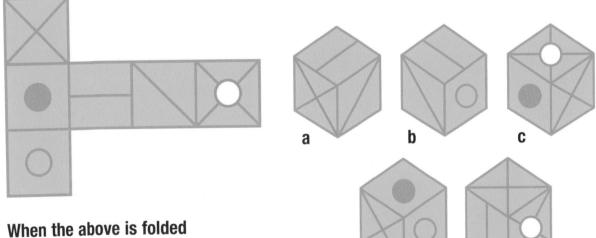

When the above is folded to form a cube, which one of the options opposite (a, b, c, d, or e) is produced?

35 DIFFICULTY ✪✪✪✪✪☆☆☆☆☆   ④ Minutes

Which of the four boxed figures (a, b, c, or d) completes the set?

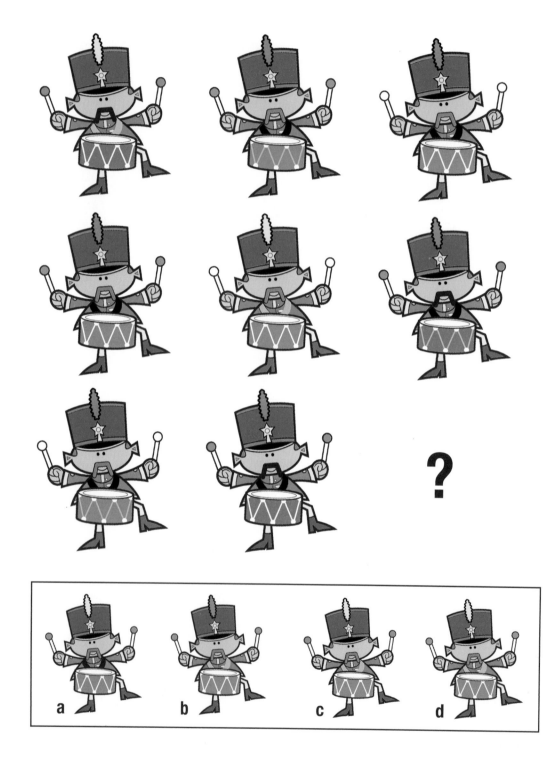

36 DIFFICULTY ✪✪✪✪✪✩✩✩✩✩   **4** Minutes

Which of the four boxed structures (a, b, c, or d) completes the set?

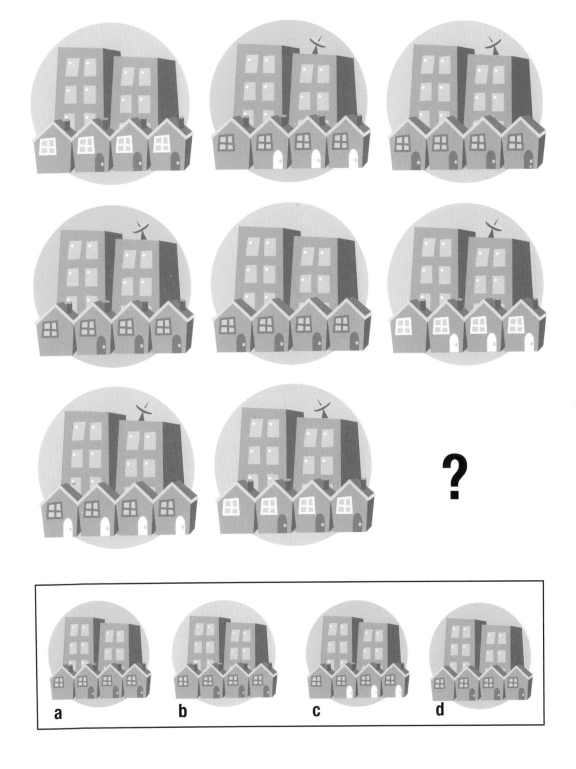

37 DIFFICULTY ★★★★★☆☆☆☆☆    **5** Minutes

Two mathematics professors meet regularly for a game of dominoes. When Professor Gauss asked his friend how many years he had been playing the game, Professor Euler replied by laying out these dominoes in a row. What was the answer?

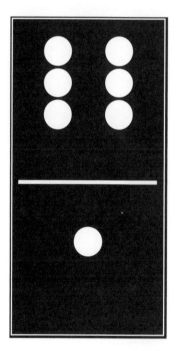

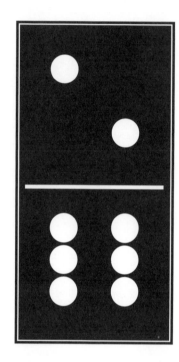

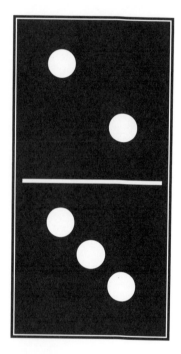

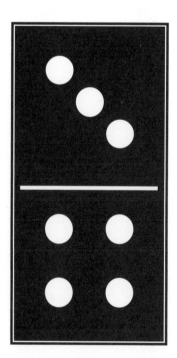

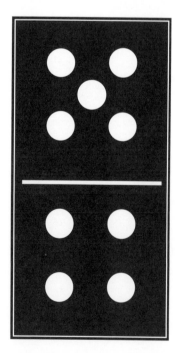

38 DIFFICULTY ●●●☆☆☆☆☆☆☆   **8** Minutes

Jane tidied her shelves the other day, then realized that she had misplaced some of the objects. Can you spot how many items from the top picture are now missing in the lower picture? Circle them in the top drawing.

39 DIFFICULTY ✪✪✪✪✪✪✩✩✩✩   ④ Minutes

Which of the figures below (a, b, c, d, e, or f) is the odd one out?

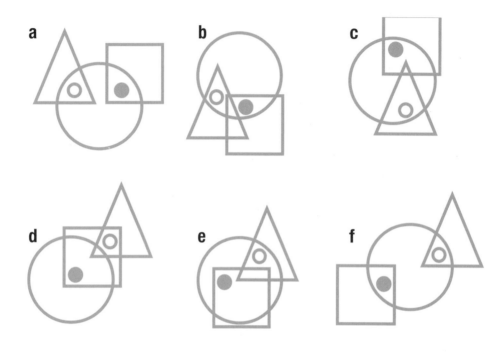

40 DIFFICULTY ✪✪✪✪✪✩✩✩✩✩   ⑥ Minutes

Can you fit the colored shapes below into the shaded area in this tangram puzzle? Pieces may be rotated, but not flipped over, and no piece may overlap another.

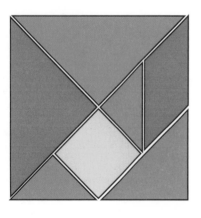

41 DIFFICULTY ✪✪✪✪✪✩✩✩✩

5 Minutes

Can you color this map using yellow, red, blue, and green only so that no two touching areas are the same? This rule doesn't apply to areas that touch at a corner point only.

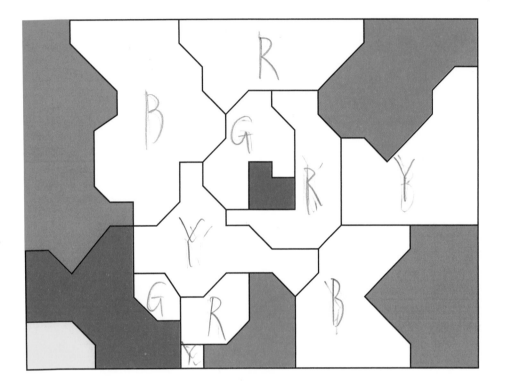

42 DIFFICULTY ✪✪✪✪✪✪✩✩✩✩

4 Minutes

What should the minute hand point to on clock d in this sequence?

a   b   c   d

43 DIFFICULTY ★★★★★★☆☆☆☆  30 Minutes

You'll be barking by the time you finish this numbergram. Make the connections between the numbers to complete the picture. See page 20 for advice on how to complete this kind of puzzle.

Column clues (reading top to bottom):

Row 1: 3 6 (near columns) ... 12
Row 2: 2 2 5 2 2 10 8 6 5 7 6   3 5   1 14   15
Row 3: 5 1 1 3 3 5 1 3 3 2 1 3 3 1 4 12 3 1 14 1 16 17   19
Row 4: 2 4 6 1 1 2 2 2 2 7 6 6 7 6 6 10 8 7 6 2 2 2 2 1 1 18 1 20 20 20

Row clues (left side, reading left to right):

		2	1
		3	2
		4	3
		4	4
	5	1	3
		7	4
		5	6
		5	8
		5	9
	2	1	11
	2	1	12
	2	1	13
		2	13
		1	14
	1	2	13
1	2	2	12
2	4	2	11
2	3	2	10
	2	3	11
2	1	6	9
	3	13	8
		20	7
	4	15	8
	2	12	6
	2	10	5
	9	2	6
	5	2	4
		2	3
		2	4
		2	1

44 DIFFICULTY ✪✪✪✪✪✪✪☆☆☆

3 Minutes

Which of the three squares below (a, b, or c) should go in the center of the grid?

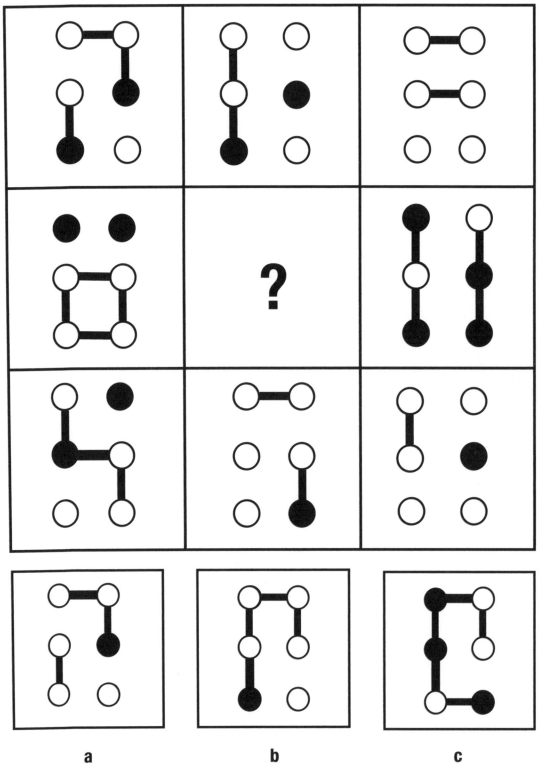

a   b   c

45 DIFFICULTY ✪✪✪✪✪☆☆☆☆☆ ⏱ 5 Minutes

When the shape below is folded to form a cube, which one of the following (a, b, c, d, or e) can be produced?

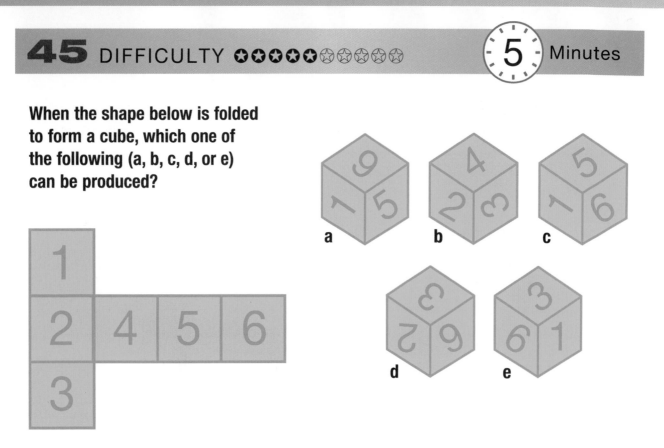

a b c

d e

46 DIFFICULTY ✪✪✪✪✪☆☆☆☆☆ ⏱ 2 Minutes

Use five matches to make five identical triangles.

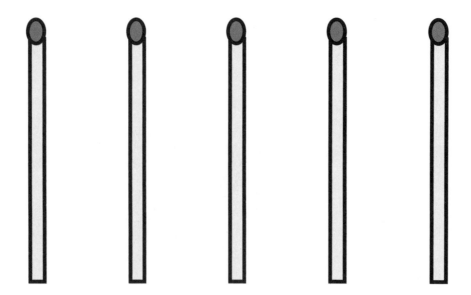

47 DIFFICULTY ✪✪✪✪✪✩✩✩✩✩ ⏱ 6 Minutes

Can you fit the colored shapes below into the shaded area in this tangram puzzle? Pieces may be rotated, but not flipped over, and no piece may overlap another.

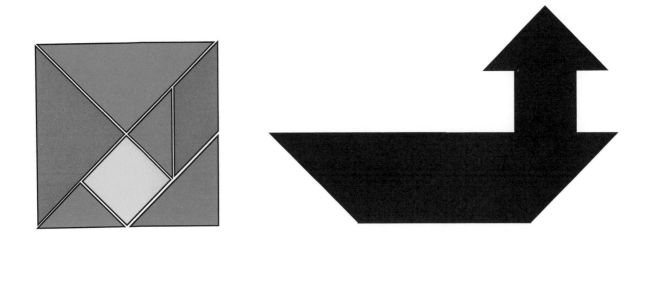

48 DIFFICULTY ✪✪✪✪✪✩✩✩✩✩ ⏱ 5 Minutes

Again, can you fit the colored shapes below into the shaded area in this tangram puzzle? Pieces may be rotated, but not flipped over, and no piece may overlap another.

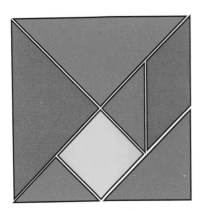

49 DIFFICULTY ✪✪✪✪✪✪✩✩✩ ⏱ **5** Minutes

Can you get from the diving board to the center of the pool through the circular maze?

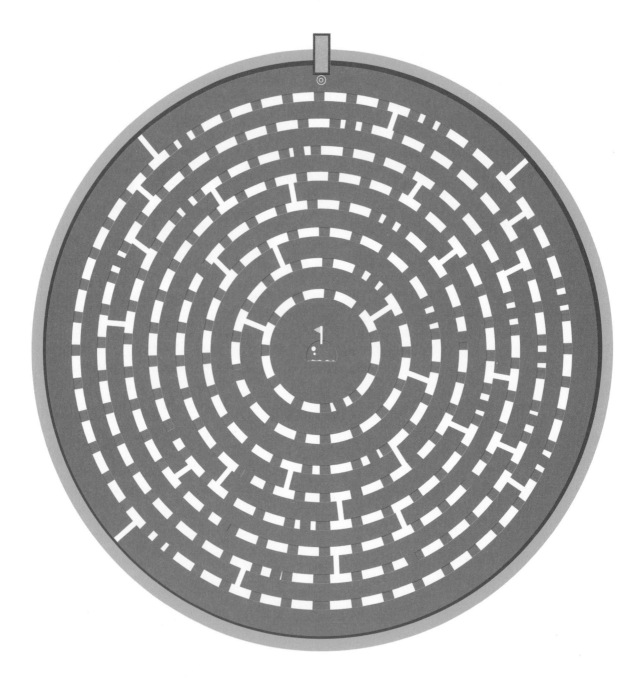

6 / Minutes

Only two of these fish are identical. Can you tell which?

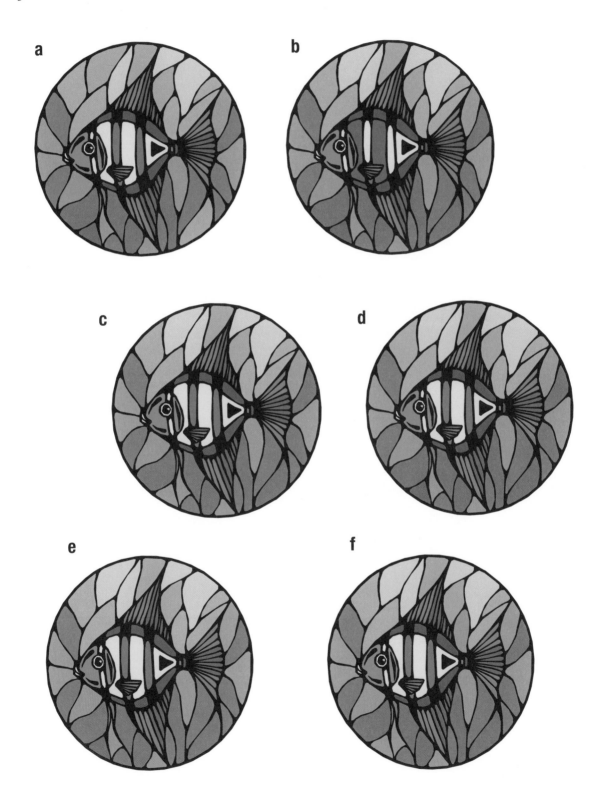

a

b

c

d

e

f

51 DIFFICULTY ✪✪✪✪✪✪☆☆☆☆ ③ Minutes

Using three straight lines only, can you divide this field into five sections, each containing two of every type of animal? Within each section, no two animals of the same type should be looking in the same direction.

52 DIFFICULTY ✪✪✪✪✪☆☆☆☆☆ ⑤ Minutes

Which four pieces can fit together to match the beach ball below? Any piece may be rotated, but not flipped over.

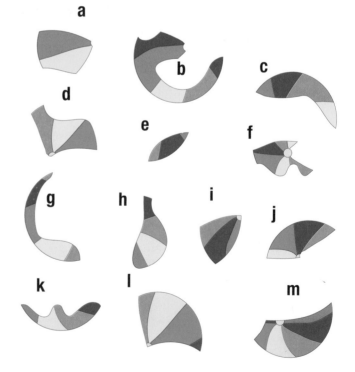

53 DIFFICULTY ✪✪✪✩✩✩✩✩✩✩ 5 Minutes

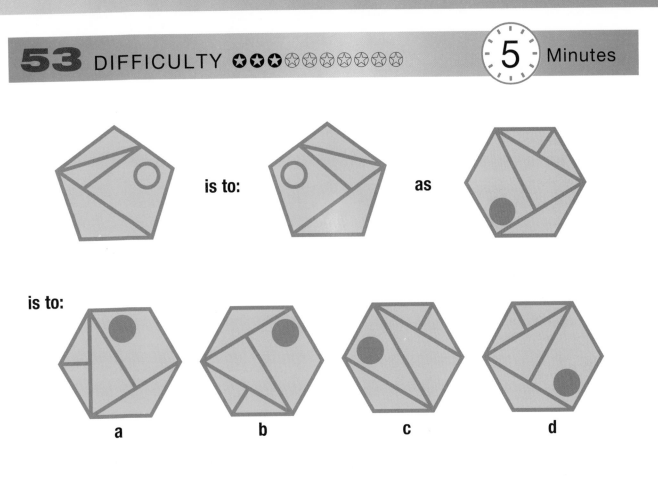

is to:

a   b   c   d

54 DIFFICULTY ✪✪✪✩✩✩✩✩✩✩ 2 Minutes

Three of the four pieces can be fitted together to form a perfect square.
Which is the odd piece out?

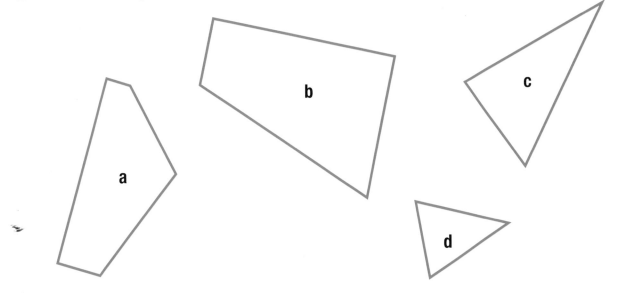

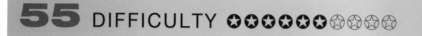

4 Minutes

When the shape below is folded to form a cube, which of the following (a, b, c, d, or e) can be produced?

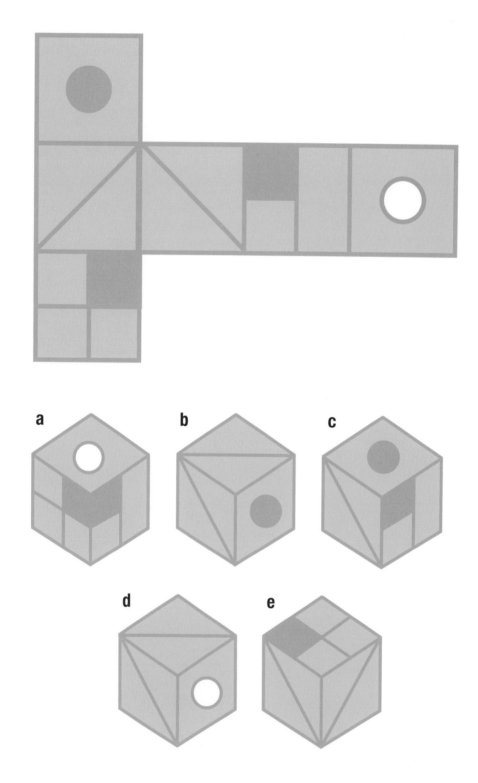

56 DIFFICULTY  2 Minutes

Study this picture for two minutes, then see if you can answer the questions on page 300.

57 DIFFICULTY 3 Minutes

Which shape (a, b, or c) goes in the empty triangle?

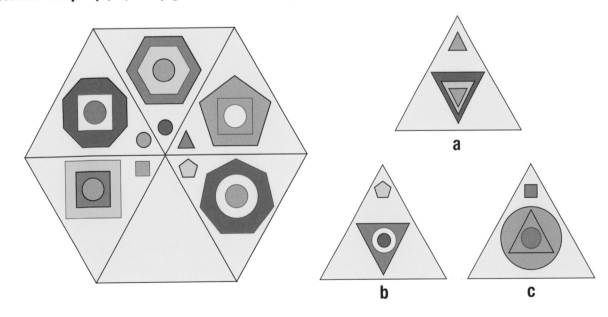

[56] DIFFICULTY ✪✪✪✪✪✪☆☆☆☆ ⏱ 2 Minutes

Can you answer these questions about the puzzle on page 299 without looking back?

1. What color is the fruit bowl?

2. Which fruit lies partially hidden behind the bowl?

3. How many limes are there in the bowl?

4. How many oranges are there in the bowl?

5. How many strawberries are there on the tray?

6. What is the total number of pieces of fruit in the bowl?

7. How many leaves are there on each apple: none, one, or two?

8. How many cherries are there on the tray?

58 DIFFICULTY ✪✪✪✪✪✪☆☆☆☆ ⏱ 3 Minutes

In pair c, where should the minute hand be pointing?

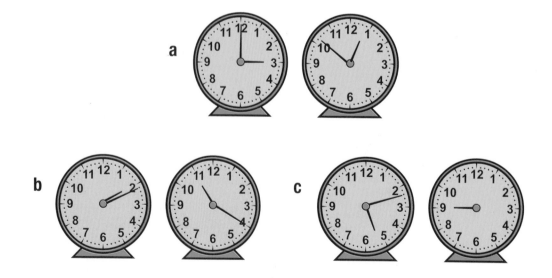

59 DIFFICULTY ✪✪✪✪✪✪☆☆☆☆  5 Minutes

Can you fit the colored shapes below into the shaded area in this tangram puzzle? Pieces may be rotated, but not flipped over, and no piece may overlap another.

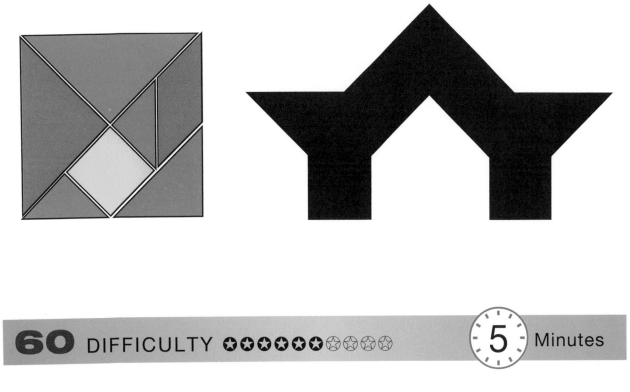

60 DIFFICULTY ✪✪✪✪✪✪☆☆☆☆ 5 Minutes

Again, can you fit the colored shapes below into the shaded area in this tangram puzzle? Pieces may be rotated, but not flipped over, and no piece may overlap another.

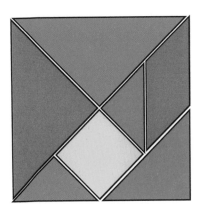

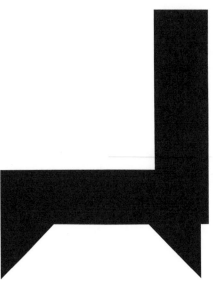

61 DIFFICULTY ●●●●○○○○○○ ⏱ 5 Minutes

Which of the four boxed figures (a, b, c, or d) completes the set?

  **?**

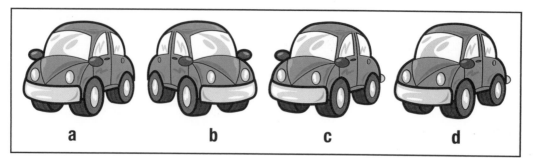

a   b   c   d

62 DIFFICULTY ✪✪✪✪✪✪✪✩✩✩

6 Minutes

Can you spot the ten differences between these two pictures? Circle them in the bottom drawing.

63 DIFFICULTY ✪✪✪✪✪✩✩✩✩✩ ④ Minutes

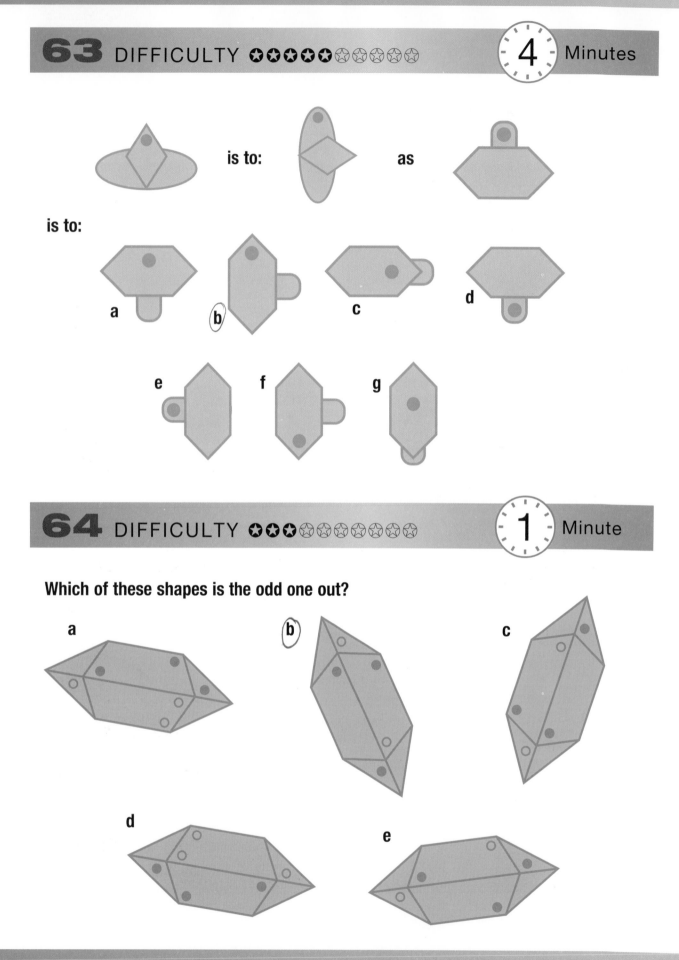

is to: as

is to:

a   b   c   d

e   f   g

64 DIFFICULTY ✪✪✪✩✩✩✩✩✩✩ ① Minute

Which of these shapes is the odd one out?

a   b   c

d   e

65 DIFFICULTY ✪✪✪✪✪✪✩✩✩✩ ⏱ 10 Minutes

In this game of solitaire, the aim is to jump one blue disk over another (horizontally or vertically), removing the disk you jumped over from the board until only one piece remains. Jumps can occur only over one disk and you must land on an empty space. The aim is to end up with just one blue disk remaining.

On this unusual board, a few of the squares are left blank. You must remain within the area marked out by the game board at all times. There may be more than one solution to the game. You could use a piece of squared paper and some coins to play this game.

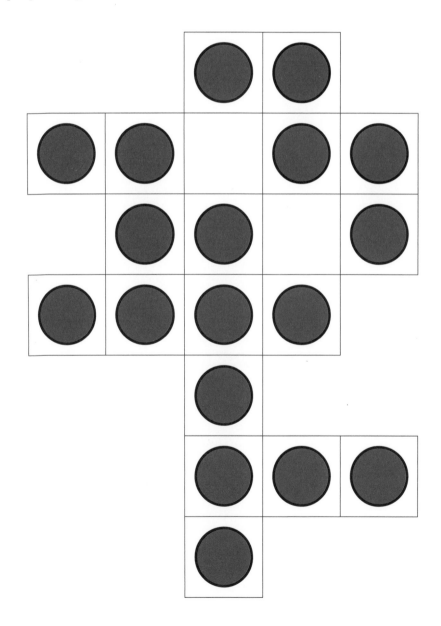

1

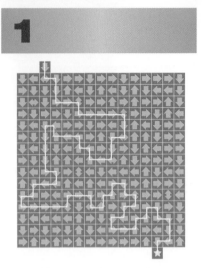

2

b; each is a square of paper with one fold.

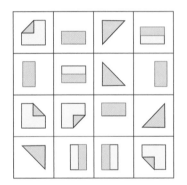

3

1. A
2. 3
3. red
4. H
5. Blue
6. Orange
7. Red
8. 14

4

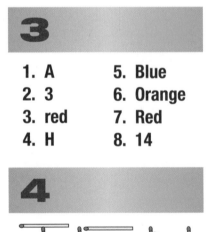

5

6

Building 1   **Building 2**

a   i

Building 3   **Building 4**

b   e

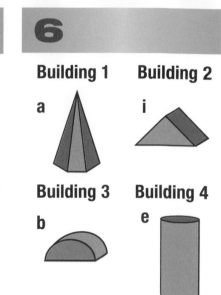

7

d; each vertical and horizontal line contains two angels with a halo and one without. Each vertical and horizontal line contains one angel with a star on her headband and two without. Each vertical and horizontal line contains two angels with white shoes and one with pink shoes. Each vertical and horizontal line contains two angels with a pink headband and one with a white headband. Each vertical and horizontal line contains two angels with a heart in her hair and one without. Each vertical and horizontal line contains two angels with a white top and one with a pink top. The missing angel should have a halo, no star on her headband, pink shoes, a pink headband, a heart in her hair, and a white top.

8

a=3, b=5, c=1, d=2, e=6, and f=4

9

8; delete one triangle and one square from each side of scale a to give 1 circle = 2 triangles. Transpose this into scale b, thus 2 squares = 3 triangles. So 4 squares + 1 circle = 6 triangles + 2 triangles = 8 triangles. Thus 8 triangles are needed to balance scale c.

10

Kirsty won in the fewest moves.

11

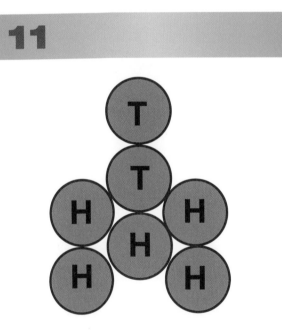

Push the central row of coins up to give two diagonal rows of heads.

12

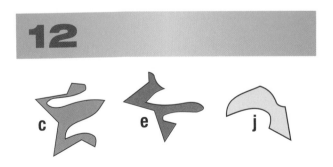

13

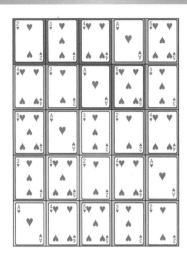

14

15

c; the cross transfers to each of the circles and the circles then go inside the square.

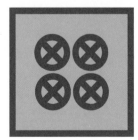

16

The tiles 5-1 and 5-2 have both been moved around 180 degrees.

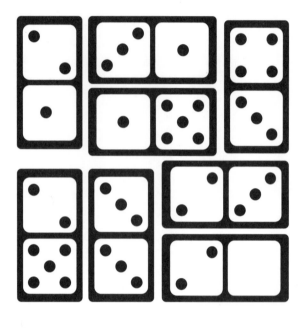

17

1=e, 2=d, 3=a, 4=f, 5=c, 6=b

18

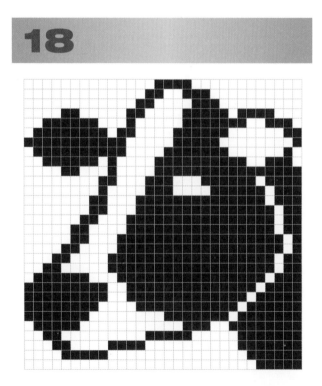

19

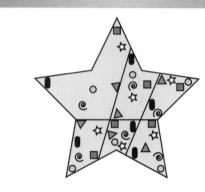

20

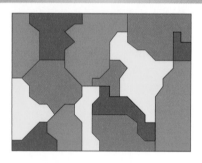

21

12; the number of minutes past the hour (shown by the minute hand) multiplied by the hour (shown by the hour hand) always equals 60: 30 x 2, 20 x 3, 10 x 6, 5 x 12.

22

d; the number of stars in each square of the middle row equals half the total of stars in the squares above and below.

23

d; blue triangles turn to white circles and vice versa.

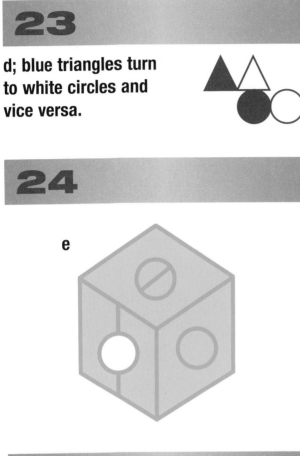

24

e

25

d; each vertical and horizontal line contains two mice with blue ears and one with white ears. Each vertical and horizontal line contains two mice with black noses and one mouse with a pink nose. Each vertical and horizontal line contains two mice with whiskers and one without. Each vertical and horizontal line contains one winking mouse and two mice that aren't winking. Each vertical and horizontal line contains two mice with tongues showing and one without. The missing mouse should have blue ears, a black nose, and whiskers. He should be winking and his tongue should be showing.

26

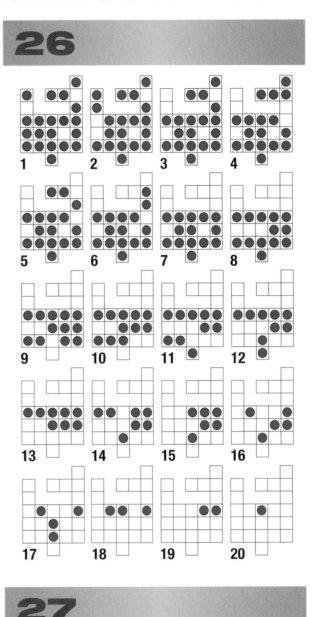

27

17:11, March 4, 2000.

28

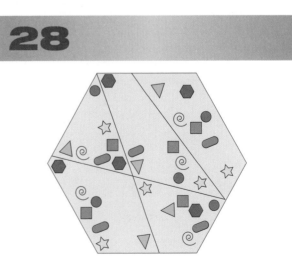

29

b and i
e and g

30

a and e

31

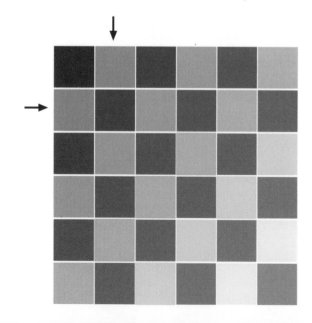

d; top moves to bottom, second moves to top, third moves to second, bottom moves to third.

33

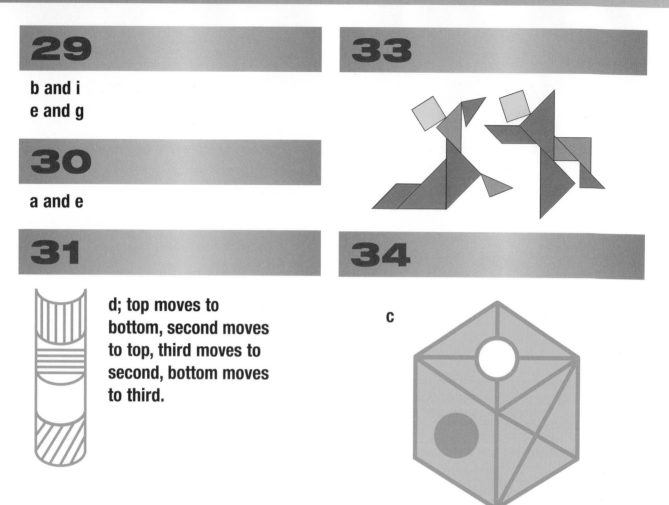

34

c

32

The two squares second from the top left corner (marked with the arrows).

35

d; each vertical and horizontal line contains one drummer with a blue drum and two with red drums. Each vertical and horizontal line contains a drum with gold cord and two with white cord. Each vertical and horizontal line contains one yellow feather and two red ones. Each vertical and horizontal line contains one black mustache and two brown ones. Each vertical and horizontal line contains two black drum straps and one gold one. Each vertical and horizontal line contains

two pairs of blue shoes and one brown pair. Each vertical and horizontal line contains a blue, a white, and a red pair of drumsticks. The missing image should be of a drummer with a red drum with white cord. He should have a yellow feather, a brown mustache, gold drum straps, blue shoes, and blue drumsticks.

36

a; each vertical and horizontal line contains one background circle in green and two in pink. Each vertical and horizontal  line contains two pictures where the houses have chimneys and one where they don't. Each vertical and horizontal line contains one picture where the house windows are white and two where they are blue. Each vertical and horizontal line contains one picture where the house doors are white and two where they are blue. Each vertical and horizontal line contains one picture where there are four doors and two where there are only three. Each vertical and horizontal line contains one satellite dish pointing left, one pointing right, and one with no dish. The missing picture should have a green background circle, chimneys on the houses, blue windows, three blue doors, and no satellite dish.

37

Nine years. Each domino expresses a fraction; when added together, the total is nine.

38

7 objects are missing.

39

d; the white dot is in the square and triangle. In all the others it is in the circle and triangle.

40

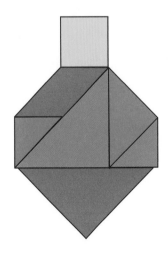

41

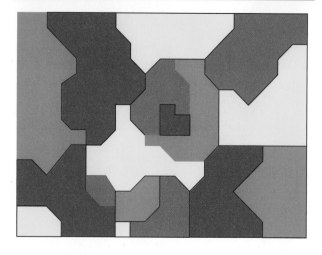

42

9; if you drew a line from the number 4 to the number 10 across the clock face, then clocks a and c would be mirror images of each other, so b and d must do likewise.

43

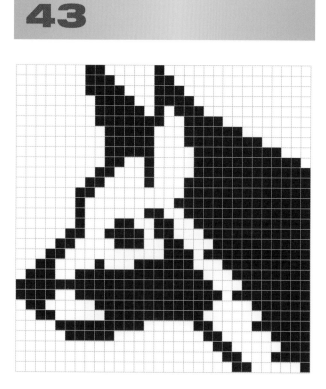

44

c; there are always as many black spots as there are vertical lines in each box.

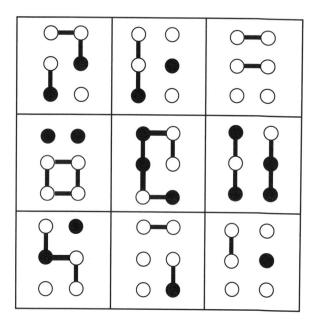

45

d

46

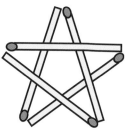

47

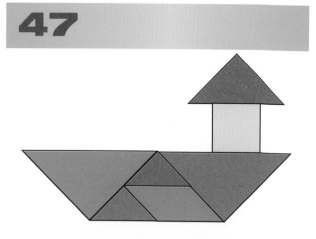

48

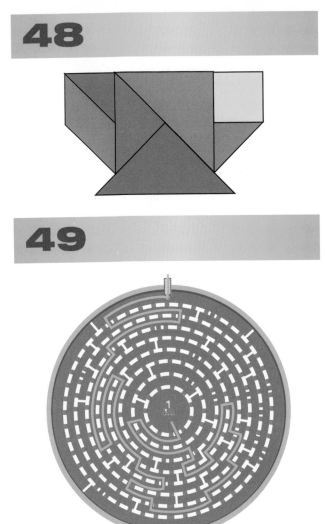

49

50

d and e

51

52

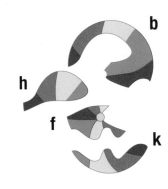

53

d; one is a mirror image of the other.

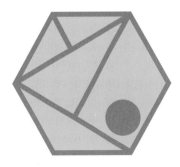

54

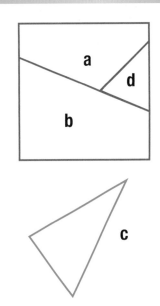

55

c

56

1. Blue
2. Banana
3. 3
4. 2
5. 9
6. 8
7. 1
8. 10

57

a; all the triangles contain a total of 4 shapes and 12 corners.

58

10; on a 24-hour clock, each of the pair is the reverse of the other:
a = 15:00/00:51, b = 02:11/11:20, and c = 05:12/21:50. (On a digital clock, each number is also the other number upside down.)

59

60

61

c; each vertical and horizontal line contains a car with a gold bumper and two with silver bumpers. Each vertical and horizontal line contains a car with a red gas cap and two with green gas caps. Each vertical and horizontal line contains two cars facing left and one facing right. Each vertical and horizontal line contains two cars with two wing mirrors and one with one wing mirror. Each vertical and horizontal line contains two cars with a rear bumper and one without a rear bumper. The missing picture should be of a car with a silver bumper and a red gas cap, facing left, with two wing mirrors and a rear bumper.

62

63

b; everything rotates 90 degrees clockwise, and the dot transfers to the top of the other figure.

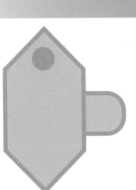

64

e; a is the same figure as d rotated and b is the same figure as c.

65

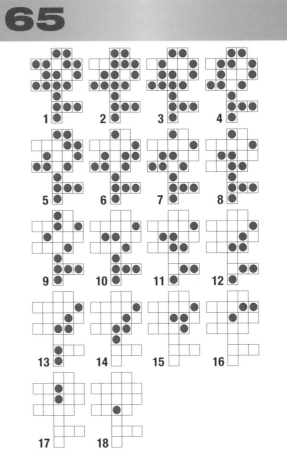

ACKNOWLEDGMENTS ✪ MIND'S EYE

✪ Puzzle contributors

Contributors are listed next to the numbers of the puzzles they created.

✪ David Bodycombe

Puzzles 20, 26, 41, 65, 70, 75, 102, 103, 105, 130

✪ Brainwarp

Puzzles 2, 4, 11, 16, 22, 32, 44, 46, 57, 95, 96, 98, 123, 128, 131

✪ Guy Campbell

Puzzles 1, 7, 15, 18, 25, 35, 36, 43, 49, 61, 77, 78, 83, 92, 97, 101, 110, 119, 120, 125, 127,

✪ Philip Carter

Puzzles 23, 24, 31, 34, 39, 45, 53, 54, 55, 63, 64, 66, 71, 80, 87, 93, 107, 112, 113

✪ Filipa de Chassey

Puzzles 62 and 109

✪ Edward Phantera

Puzzles 29, 30, 50, 72, 88, 89, 100, 117

✪ Puzzle Press Ltd

Puzzles 3, 5, 6, 8, 9, 10, 12, 13, 14, 17, 19, 28, 51, 52, 56, 68, 82, 85, 86, 90, 104, 106, 111, 115, 116, 118, 121, 122, 126, 129

✪ Justin Scroggie

Puzzles 21, 27, 37, 42, 58, 74, 79, 84, 94, 99

✪ Sunrise Puzzles

Puzzles 33, 40, 47, 48, 59, 60, 67, 69, 73, 76, 81, 91, 108, 114, 124

Mind's Eye was commissioned, edited, designed, and produced by:
Book Creation Ltd., 20 Lochaline Street, London W6 9SH, United Kingdom
Managing Director: Hal Robinson
Editor: David Popey **Art Editor:** Keith Miller
Designer: Mark Sayer **Copy Editors:** Sarah Barlow and Ali Moore